Miles Kington's Motorway Madness

Miles Kington's Motorway Madness

A Traveller's Treasury

Miles Kington

HarperCollins*Publishers*

HarperCollins*Publishers*
77–85 Fulham Palace Road,
Hammersmith, London W6 8JB

Published by HarperCollins*Publishers* 1998
1 3 5 7 9 8 6 4 2

A catalogue record for this book is
available from the British Library

ISBN 0 00 255912 9

Set in Meridien

Printed in Great Britain by
Scotprint Ltd, Musselburgh

Contents

Foreword

This is it! Yes, at last you have a motorway book which you can handle with pride! A motorway book you can give each other for Christmas, birthdays or even long stays in hospital! A motorway book which will not look out of place emerging from wrapping paper!

Oh, there have been plenty of motorway books before. There have been Motorway Atlases, showing you the exits where you can come on but not go off. There have been books about 'Pubs Quite Near to Motorway Exits', showing you how to get away from motorway service areas by slipping off motorways to have lunch at quiet country pubs which turn out to be absolutely jammed solid by purchasers of copies of 'Pubs Quite Near to Motorway Exits'. In the cookery field there was even the 'Watford Gap 100 Favourite Recipes Cook Book'! (Just kidding.)

But now at last there is a book which for the first time celebrates the culture of the motorway. The motorway we all know so well, with its glories and horrors. The motorway of the open road and the endless tailback, the inexplicable cones, and the wonderful signs saying 'Sorry For Any Delay'. The motorway with all its mysteries, like why the telephones in motorway service areas are so often right next to the noisiest possible bit, the video games corridor. Like, is there a place called *North* Mimms? Like, do all motorway service areas have a secret exit and entrance for the employees and fire brigade to use, but which we never get to see?

Like, why are there more cows crossing bridges over motorways than there are in the fields on either side?

The motorway which we all love and hate so much but which we have never seen described in any book before. Now, the whole culture of the motorway is celebrated in this *Traveller's Treasury*!

10 GREAT MOTORWAY FILMS

No 1.
Gone With The Wind

Ever notice those signs saying 'Beware Cross Winds'? Ever thought how unlikely it was that your trailer or caravan could actually be blown away? That's what Dorothy thought, too. So when her mobile home was sent spinning away into the sky off the viaduct she got the surprise of her life – but not half the surprise she got when she landed on the Wicked Witch of the North!

How a Motorway is Named

Before a motorway can be given a name, there has to be a discussion at the highest level. It goes something like this.

'What shall we call this new motorway?'
  'What did we call the last one?'
  'Umm, the M53, I think.
  'Well, this one should be the M54, shouldn't it?'
  'No, that's not quite how it works, Your Royal Highness. We don't number them in order. We generally like to name a motorway after the nearest big road it is shadowing.'
  'So the M4 is called the M4 because it parallels the A4?'
  'That's it, Your Royal Highness.'
  'How extraordinary! Is that why there is no M7?'
  'I'm sorry?'
  'There is an M6 and an M8 but no M7. Is that because there is no motorway shadowing the A7?'
  'Exactly so, Your Royal Highness.'
  'That's very, very interesting.'
  'Thank you.'
  'Incidentally, why was it called the A4 in the first place?'
  'Why was what called the A4 in the first place?'
  'The A4.'

'Ah. Well, of course it wasn't called the A4 in the first place.'

'Wasn't it ? Then what was it called?'

'The Old Bath Road.'

'Good heavens. That's amazing.'

'That is, it wasn't called the Old Bath Road originally. That came later. First it was called the Bath Road. Then it became old later.'

'Extraordinary.'

'Yes.'

'So what are we going to call this new motorway?'

'Why don't you just leave that to us, Your Royal Highness?'

'Very good idea. I will.'

OLD MOTORWAY SAYINGS

Leigh Delamere, Leigh Delamere,
Isn't either there nor here,
Halfway there and halfway back,
Leigh Delamere's neither white nor black.
London and Bristol are next to the pond,
But Leigh Delamere is back of beyond.

Motorway Nursery Rhymes

THIS OLD MAN

This old man he played one
He backed into my Shogun
    With a knick knack paddy whack
    Give the dog a bone
    This old man came rolling home

This old man he played two
He crashed into my Subaru
    With a knick knack paddy whack
    Etc., etc., etc.

This old man, he played three
Kicked out by the RAC,
    With a knick knack paddy whack
    Etc., etc., etc.

This old man, he played four,
He wrote off my Saab four door
    With a knick knack paddy whack
    Etc., etc., etc.

This old man he went five
Dented my new four-wheel drive
    With a knick knack paddy whack
    Etc., etc., etc

Make Your Diary a Motorway Diary!

Here are some great motorway dates and festivals to cut out and put on the right day in your diary!

17 January
Feast of St Norbert, patron saint of overtaking on the inside.

27 February
Anniversary of the day in 1987 on which Gary Rothwell of Luton became the first man ever to throw a frisbee across six lanes of motorway traffic without hitting anything. (He had earlier been the first man to go to prison for <u>nearly</u> throwing a frisbee across six lanes of traffic and hitting a small mini-van which swerved and caused the great M1 pile-up of 1985.)

23 March
Day in 1955 on which it was decided that motorways would be coloured blue on maps.

1 April
All Fools Day – the day on which one is allowed to say to *any* policeman who has pulled you over for speeding, 'Pull the other one, copper, I know what day it is!'

3 April
Feast of St Lollobridget, patron saint of Italian lorry drivers eating British motorway food for the first time.

17 April
No Overtaking Day (except Wales).

22 April
Round the M25 race (unofficial).

5 May
Anniversary of setting of record for largest fish ever caught on a British motorway (see Flooding of M25, 5 May 1986).

12 May
Roads leading to Ireland crowded with Eurovision Song Contest traffic.

17 May
Road Rage Absolution Service, Canterbury Cathedral (sorry, NO crash helmets inside cathedral).

14 June
National No-Waving-From-Back-Windows-Of-Coaches Day.

29 June
Anniversary of the only recorded vision on a motorway – the appearance of the Blessed Virgin Mary in 1981 to a seven-year-old child at service area in Lancashire. Mary is reported to have said to the child, 'Come on, love, eat up your dinner properly and you'll get a lolly!' and then vanished. However, the vision was never accepted by the Vatican.

23 August
Help-A-Toad-Across-The-Motorway-By-The-Nearest-Bridge Day.

26 August
Free-style Motorway Cone-Throwing Contest, Newport Pagnell Fayre.

1 September
Day of the Lower Widrington Walk. (The inhabitants of Lower Widrington, a village in Yorkshire, insist that they still have the right to use a public footpath which used to cross the nearby motorway. On this day, every year, they repeatedly walk across the motorway at this point, bringing the traffic to a standstill.)

29 September

Beginning of autumn season of Motorway Navigation Classes at most local colleges.

14 October

Feast of St Roberta, patron saint of lawnmowers and all other vehicles banned from motorways.

15 October

Drive-Slow-For-Peace-Day on M40. (This is an annual event but it is also celebrated twice daily on the M25.)

22 October

Battle of Charnock Richard.

23 October

Beginning of autumn; mileage counters go back.

24 October

Annual appearance of ghost of Sir Ernest Marples on many bridges on M1.

3 November

Christmas Illuminations go on in all motorway services areas.

1 December

Beginning of annual fortnight's closing of Motorway Museum, with sign saying: 'Motorway Museum closed – Sorry For Any Inconvenience'.

10 December

Last Christmas posting day to European service areas.

15 December

Last Christmas posting day to Scottish motorways.

18 December

Last Christmas posting Day to all other motorway service areas.

20 December

Carol services on many bridges overlooking motorways.

24 December

Most service areas closed for the Annual Christmas Parties, at which the managers do all the cooking and serving, and staff are waited on by them.

30 December

Time to peel all these entries out of your old diary and stick them in your new one.

What, you may ask, does verse have to do with motorways? Good question. But there is also a good answer. Everything! Or at least it should have. Motorways are central to our lives, and so should poetry be. Poetry should be taken away from the poets and given back to the driver of the Ford Fiesta – though it could well be that the driver of the Ford Fiesta may not want to have poetry given back to him. But even he must have noticed that the rhythms of motorway life are all around us. The regular swish of the windscreen wiper, the thwack of the wheels on the speed-reducing strips, the repetitive signs (Services 2M, Services 1M, Services Half Mile, then the three strips, two strips, one strip…) – even the predictable way in which that coach we left miles behind keeps overtaking us again has its own regular rhythm. There's something very traditional and old-fashioned about life on a motorway, anyway. That's why the ballad is the form best suited to motorway life. That's why T. S. Eliot would have been a rotten motorway poet. No rhyme, no rhythm, no reason, all free verse and all over the place. (Of course, even T. S. Eliot, when he came to his senses, wrote proper poetry, proper rhyming and scannng poetry, proper poetry about cats, poetry you could put on the West End stage, poetry that Andrew Lloyd Webber could put a tune to! Cats, yes, but will there ever be a West End musical of 'The Waste Land'? I think not. Will these motorway verses attract the attention of Andrew Lloyd Webber? Sir Andrew Lloyd Webber, I mean? Well, stranger things have happened…)

The Ballad of the Man on the Motorway Bridge

When my daily work is done
I like to have a spot of fun
So after I've packed away my gear
I pop down the pub for a bit of cheer.
(I normally go to one of CAMRA's
Where the landlord's nice and the barmaid's glamorous.)
Well, as I was sitting at the bar,
Drinking the first of many a jar,
I heard the bloke right by me say:
'I drove from Birmingham today.
Along the motorway I came,
Avoiding Oxford, then past Thame,
And I saw the most extraordinary sight –
I'll swear it wasn't a trick of the light –
But on every bridge I went below
There was a picturesque tableau.
Up above me, in mid-air,
Momentarily frozen there,
Against the light, in silhouette,
The prettiest pictures you could get,

17

Of sheep and shepherd, pony and trap,
Old bucolic types in cap,
Herds of cows on milking bent,
Led by an agricultural gent
Wearing a kind of smock, I'll swear,
Or else Victorian underwear!
Every bloody bridge I passed
Had its full supporting cast
Acting out a rural scene –
Rummest thing I've ever seen!'
'Is that so odd?' his friend replied,
'The country's where cows and sheep reside!
That's where you find farm animals!
Not in towns or shopping malls!
They're all out there in the countryside!
No wonder you saw them walk or ride
Across the bridge on the motorway!
It's home sweet home for them, night and day!
It's where they live! Their habitat!
Don't you see what I'm getting at?'
The first man blushed, and stuck to his guns.
'Maybe you think that I'm a dunce
But these tableaux I'm harping on
Were only a bridge phenomenon.
No such groupings did I see
Behind or either side of me.
Every field to west or east
Was totally devoid of beast.
But almost every bridge I spied
Came with tableau pre-supplied.
Man on bike, girl on pony,

Woman called Joan and man called Tony,
Boy with dog, couple with pram,
Girl called Sue, boy called Sam...
Every bridge was full up there,
Otherwise the country was bare.
Well, that's not natural, that's not right.
That's what I'd call a sinister sight.
Why should bridges teem and rave,
While the landscape's silent as the grave?'
A painful silence then ensued,
(Broken only by drink and food)
Until I leant across to them
And diffidently said: 'Ahem!
I've been listening to you natter,
And I think I can help you in this matter.
I know why those bridges are so packed.
I know who does it, as a matter of fact.'
The drinkers looked at me and gaped.
From one of them a sound escaped
Which roughly meant, 'Who the hell are you?
And if you know it, tell us who!'
I smiled a smile of secrecy
And said mysteriously, 'It's me... '

*The poem goes on for many a weary line further, in which the narrator
explains that he works for the English Tourist Board, and it is his job each
day to superintend those delightful little rural processions which we have
often seen wending their way over motorway bridges, to give motorists the
illusion that there is still an English countryside out there somewhere, but
whether he is telling the truth or pulling their leg we never find out.*

10 GREAT MOTORWAY FILMS

No 2.
The Lost Weekend

They set out from Sidcup in Kent to visit their cousins in Preston. Yes, it was one wintry Friday evening in January when they set out. North of London it was snowing hard. A bit further north it was snowing very, very hard. They never got any further north than that, because they were snowed in at a service area for three days. At first everyone trapped there was friends but by the end of the weekend half the children had gone missing, all the women were weeping and most of the men were playing poker for the last apfelstrudel left in Julie's Pantry. Sunday night the road was clear again, so they went south back to Sidcup. It isn't a weekend they ever talked about again.

THE MOTORWAY MURDER

**A Completely
NEW
Hercule Poirot
Thriller**

by

*g*th* Chr*st**

'At first sight it was a baffling mystery,' said Hercule Poirot, looking round at the gathered company. 'Tout à fait incroyable. A man drives into a motorway service area to get some petrol. He fills the car with petrol but he does not pay. Instead he shoots himself at the wheel. The cashier gets worried after ten minutes when the car is still parked by the petrol pump. With a man apparently asleep at the wheel. She goes and has a look. He is dead. But there is no gun in the car.'

There was dead silence. This was indeed how Simon Garfunkle had died. All alone in his red saloon car, at the petrol pump. Nobody now present was sorry. They had all wanted him dead for one reason or another.

'So the police are sent for. They arrive. They are puzzled. Murder is not their normal diet on the motorway. Oh, to be sure many people would like to kill each other on the motorway, but they so seldom get the chance – am I right? So, the police are not sure what to do. Luckily, who should pull in for petrol a few minutes later than M. Hercule Poirot, the well-known sleuth? So, after a little persuasion I am agreeable to help investigate.'

Poirot looked at the faces again. They were all tight with attention. He had asked all the suspects to gather in the magnificent library of Badgers Castle motorway service area to hear his conclusions regarding the crime, and they had all come. Some had come unwillingly, but they had all come...

'Bon. Now, one thing strikes me straightaway. There is no gun in the car, so Monsieur Garfunkle has not shot himself. Perhaps he has shot himself on the motorway, thrown the gun away, driven to the petrol station and then died? No, I think not. Therefore he was shot, yes, but by someone else. By someone who was in the car with him. By someone who wanted him dead.'

'But surely... ' the silence was broken by Joyce, the dead man's widow, '... but surely if Simon had had a companion, someone would have seen him!'

'Not at all, Madame Garfunkle,' said Poirot. 'People come and people go in a petrol station. To be precise, several hundred every hour. Not even I could remember half those faces. No, no, I think we can assume that the dead man drove in to the petrol station, and that his companion got out to fill the car with petrol. We know this to be true because the car was, indeed, full of petrol.'

'So, to sum up for slower readers,' said Major Hastings with care, 'the late Simon Garfunkle was found shot dead in his car at this service area. He couldn't have committed suicide. He must have been murdered. The murderer must have driven in with him, shot him, then gone off, leaving no clue behind.'

'Hold on a moment,' said the Bishop of Warwick, the dead man's uncle. 'Why on earth do you think I might have killed him?'

'Did I say so, Bishop?' said Poirot sharply, turning his unblinking gaze on him. 'We have not come to the motive yet, Bishop! We have only got as far as weapon and opportunity. Motive comes later. Please wait your turn! There is a certain protocol in these affairs.'

'I'm sorry,' mumbled the Bishop.

'One would think that you had never gathered in the library after a murder with the other suspects before,' said Poirot dryly.

'I never have,' said the Bishop apologetically.

'Ciel...' said Poirot. 'Then kindly leave things to those who have. Now, are there any questions so far?'

'Yes,' said Lady Rowena Garfunkle, whose title Simon would have inherited had he lived, and had four others died. 'You said that it was the murderer who bought the petrol. Might there not be some clue in a cheque or credit card voucher which he left behind?'

'Trés bon,' said Poirot. 'You think better than these others, madame. Well done! Yes, we did think of that, and we investigated names of people who had recently bought petrol there. I wonder if you can guess what we discovered. We discovered that *every single one of you here in this room had been in that filling station in the previous ten minutes*! Everyone! Buying varying amounts of petrol!'

There was a communal gasp that could only be called audible. And communal as well, of course.

'All of you had been there,' said Poirot. 'Lady Rowena. Joyce Garfunkle. The Bishop of Warwick. Nigel Messenger. Hugh Ingot-Smith. Lady Semolina Tempest. And last, but not least, Lord Rupert Dunkerley. Quite a nice coincidence, don't you think? You were all there and you all wished for Simon's death!'

'I thought we hadn't come on to motive yet, Poirot, old bean,' said the cheery voice of young Lord Rupert Dunkerley.

'Touché,' said Poirot. 'But the big question for me, is this. How did the murderer leave the petrol station, the scene of his murder? It is difficult for him, you see. He arrives in Simon's car. He shoots Simon. He leaves. But the car is still there. *So how did he leave*?'

'Are you suggesting,' said Lady Rowena stiffly, 'that the murderer was driven away by one of us, all of whom had apparently been there in the previous ten minutes and therefore had ample opportunity to spirit him away?'

'Again, very logical, madame, but this time quite wrong. I am suggesting something quite different. I am suggesting that the murderer never left the service area at all.'

'Never left at all?' said Major Ernest Garfunkle, whom we don't seem to have mentioned so far. 'But that would mean he was still here!'

'Yes.'

'But that's baloney!'

'Why?' purred Poirot.

'Because the murder took place five days ago and if a chap hung

round a service area for five days, people would start to notice.'

'Not if he worked there,' said Poirot.

The puzzled silence was broken by a knock at the library door. At Poirot's command to enter, the door opened and a handsome man in RAC recruiting uniform came in.

'You wanted to see me, sir?'

'My God – it's Geoffrey!'

It was the Bishop of Warwick who spoke. And everyone else in the room except Poirot and Hastings echoed his gasp of recognition. It was Geoffrey Garfunkle, Simon's ne'er-do-well younger brother who hadn't been heard of for over two years. Geoffrey looked round the table and slowly grinned.

'Well, I'll be … if this isn't the rummest family reunion I ever saw. Aunt Rowena … Joyce … Bishop … Rupe … welcome to my little service area…"

'Do you know why we are all here?' asked Poirot.

'Not the faintest. Is it my birthday?'

'It would be very easy for the murderer to evade detection if he worked here,' went on Poirot, not looking at Geoffrey. 'If he was, let us say, an RAC officer in charge of recruiting. It is not a rewarding job trying to get people to join up. Many, many people say no, I do not want to join the RAC. Many people do not even make eye contact as they go inside. This must be humiliating in the long run. Especially if the person is your brother. Especially if your brother repeatedly refuses to join the RAC just to make your day. You must come to hate him.'

'Yes!' burst in Geoffrey, his RAC badge shining in the gloom of the library, with rays from the open fire glinting off it. 'I hated Simon! He knew I worked here as an RAC man and it delighted him to stop for petrol or a break as often as possible and laugh in my face when I asked him to join. It was cruel! But the cruellest thing of all was when

Simon joined the AA, right in front of me, two weeks ago!'

'So you killed him?' said the Bishop quietly. 'Just because he would not join the RAC?'

Geoffrey laughed. 'Kill Simon? Never! I would not soil my hands on him!'

'Then who…?' asked Lady Rowena.

'It surprises me,' said Poirot. 'It surprises me very much. It surprises me very much that none of you is surprised. Après tout, I tell you that all of you here turn up at the same petrol station within ten minutes and nobody seems at all astounded by this. Nobody says, mon Dieu, quelle coincidence! What an amazing chain of chance! You all take it like lambs. And shall I tell you why?'

There was silence.

'Because you planned it. Because you all met here for a purpose. Because you all planned to get together to kill Simon Garfunkle. And because you carried out that murder perfectly and then fled. However, there was one fatal flaw in your plan. A witness.'

There was more silence.

'None of you knew that Geoffrey was working here as an RAC man. None of you recognised him.'

'It's true,' said Geoffrey, nodding. 'One after the other I saw my whole family trooping in and out of the main building, all separately. Rupert … the Bish … Lady Semolina … all of them. None of them recognised me as they are all snobs and do not look at RAC men. I didn't say hello to them because I didn't want anyone to know what I was doing. Having Simon know was bad enough…'

There was the same silence, but more of it.

'Just one thing, Monsieur Poirot.' It was Lady Semolina Tempest, who had not yet spoken. Poirot had not been sure she was awake. He was not entirely sure if she were alive. She was very old, but, as it now turned out, she still had her wits about her.

'There is one thing that puzzles me. If we had all met in one place to murder Simon, why on earth did we all pay by credit card and thus give away our identity, and our presence? It was like signing a death warrant.'

'The very same thing occurred to me,' said Poirot. 'It is the very thing which has been exercising my grey cells. Why should people who have gathered for a murder establish their presence instead of concealing it? This is not the way that Simon's murderers would have behaved.'

'So what did your little grey cells tell you, O Wise Belgian?' murmured Hugh Ingot-Smith.

Poirot glanced at him sharply before replying.

'My little grey cells told me that you all gathered at that service area for a reason. But it was not for the purpose of murdering Simon Garfunkle! Ah, no! It was for the purpose of establishing an alibi.'

'An alibi?' said Geoffrey Garfunkle the RAC officer, sinking into a vacant chair. 'What did they all want an alibi for?'

'For the murder of Lady Ingot-Smith.'

'WHAT? My mother?' Hugh Ingot-Smith sat up.

'Oh, yes,' said Poirot. 'There was never any intention to murder Simon Garfunkle. They all wanted to murder your mother, for reasons too complex to explain now. But while the deed was being carried out, they decided to establish an alibi at the Badgers Castle service area. So they could prove their innocence.'

'Look, you've got it all wrong,' said Hugh Ingot-Smith. 'My mother is alive! I spoke to her this morning!'

'Yes,' said Poirot. 'The murder never took place. Although it was planned in detail, the murderer's courage failed at the last moment and he came back to report failure.'

'And who was he?'

'Simon Garfunkle, of course,' said Poirot. 'He came back to the service station to report failure and you were all so incensed that you did away with him there and then.'

There was another silence, even more silent than the other silences.

'And who pulled the trigger?' said Geoffrey, taking off his RAC cap and putting it on the table.

'You did,' said Poirot.

'*Me*?' said Geoffrey. 'That's impossible! I am the only innocent person here! Why would I want to kill Simon under the eyes of all his family?'

'Partly to impress them and partly,' said Poirot, 'because you are not Geoffrey Garfunkle at all. You are, in truth, the elder brother of Hugh Ingot-Smith who has been missing for ten years after your father, the late Lord Ingot-Smith…'

But this was too much to take, or even too much to follow, and, enraged by Poirot's increasingly complicated theories, the gathered relations rose as one person, advanced on Poirot and did away with him. Fearful that his friend Major Hastings might report this, they did away with him as well.

Luckily, they had all thought beforehand that something like this might happen, so they had all fixed very good alibis at a Happy Eater on the A303 near Warminster and none of them was ever suspected of the great detective's death.

Motorway Nursery Rhymes

MARY, MARY, QUITE CONTRARY

Mary, Mary, quite contrary,
    Why do you drive so slow?
Oh, I try to annoy other drivers
    As on my way I go.

I flash my indicator
    And then I don't pull out
Which tends to create in others
    An element of doubt

When someone else is passing
    I like to accelerate
And then they can't get past me –
    That's something they all hate.

Mary, Mary, quite contrary,
    How do you drive your car?
Oh, I drive it very slowly
    And I drive it very far.

The
Famous Five
on the
Motorway

A New Children's Classic

'Gosh – what a lovely little cottage!' said Ann, as they turned the corner of the lane. There in front of them, stood Motorway View, the holiday cottage where they were to stay for the next five weeks.

'We're so lucky to be on holiday together again,' said Julian. 'It's a real stroke of luck that none of our parents ever want to have us around at holiday time but would rather pack us all off together!'

'And when you consider that they don't see us during term time either,' said Dick, 'it's a wonder that they even recognise us.'

'Mmm,' said Ann, trying to remember what her father looked like. 'Gosh, who's this?'

Out of the front door of the cottage came an apple-cheeked woman who put on a broad smile when she saw the four children.

'Why, you'll be Julian, Dick, Ann, Georgina and Timmy the dog,' she said, cheerfully. 'I'm Mrs Wentworth and you're the children I'm expecting!'

'It's one thing to be pregnant,' said Julian, 'but to be expecting four children and a dog is something else!'

Nobody understood the joke and nobody laughed.

Not for the first time, Julian wondered if he weren't getting too old for all this.

'By the way, I'm George, not Georgina,' said George crossly. 'Please don't ever call me Georgina!'

'George wants to be a boy when she grows up,' explained Dick. 'She's saving up for the operation now, but it's very expensive.'

'Well, never mind,' said motherly Mrs Wentworth. 'Come along in and have some tea. Oh, just a few words of warning before you settle in. Mr Wentworth, my husband, may seem a bit grumpy at first but that's only because he's got a heart of gold. My son Barry may seem hostile at first but that's only because he's jealous of your camaraderie. And, whatever you do, don't ever, ever go down to the old service area!'

'Old service area?' said George. 'That sounds interesting!'

'Where is it?' said Dick.

'Down there on the motorway,' said Mrs Wentworth, 'there used to be a service area called Leigh Pemberton. It's all closed down now, hasn't been in use for twenty years, but the buildings are all still there, the games arcade, and filling station, and RAC recruiting officer's hut and everything, only it's all closed off because it's dangerous, so don't ever try to get in there, because it's out of bounds, see, and if I ever hear that any of you has been nosing around in there, I'll have your guts for garters, so I will!'

Just for a moment kind Mrs Wentworth's face contorted with rage and fury, then it melted back to her normal placid mien.

'Gosh!' said Ann, a little bit later. 'I wonder why she seemed so cross about the old service area. She seemed very keen that we shouldn't go down there. Do you think she knows something we don't know?'

'Everybody knows something that nobody else knows,' said Julian. 'No two single pools of knowledge are identical. We all have private areas of cognition. You see, Jonathan Miller says…'

The others looked at Julian oddly. Sometimes they wondered if he shouldn't be replaced by a younger person.

Then, suddenly, George, who had gone for a walk by herself, came running back up the field, shouting and waving, with Timmy barking at her heels.

'I've just seen something really extraordinary at the old service area,' she panted. 'Lights!'

'Of course you saw lights, silly,' said Dick. 'It's the cars going back and forth on the motorway under the old bridge. The service area may be closed, but the road is still open!'

'No!' said George. 'It wasn't cars! It was people actually inside the service area! They were signalling! and I think they were signalling to someone up here!'

Gosh! What is the mystery of the deserted service area? Is a gang of thieves using it as a depot for stolen Italian church art en route to a big auction house in London? Is it being used as an illicit premises for bare knuckle fighting? Have TV people moved in to use it as a location for an episode of The Bill? Is another gang of children called the Secret Six, staying at another cottage nearby, just using it as a place to play games? Or did Mr Forte simply forget to turn out one or two of the lights when he closed down the place twenty years ago? Don't miss the next episode of 'The Famous Five on the Motorway'!

The Ballad of the Middle Laner

When I was but a little lad,
I asked this question of my Dad:
'Oh, Dad, one thing can you explain –
Why do we drive in the middle lane?

'Would it be a great mistake
If we pulled out to overtake?
Or would it really be so bad
If we were in the slow lane, Dad?'

My father said to me, 'I'm sorry,
I *will* not imitate a lorry,
Nor will I drive like a railway train –
The place for us is the middle lane.'

Oh, I'm a middle laner,
I love the middle lane,
I drive down it to Dover
And drive right back again.

You can flash your blooming headlights
And hoot till you go insane,
But you'll never get me moving
From out the middle lane.

And now that I'm a full grown man
I think I understand God's plan;
That some are naturally fast or slow,
But most down the middle lane should go.

And even when no car's in sight,
And I could pull to left or right,
I hear the little voice of Fate:
'You stay right in the middle, mate!'

And now, when my son, whose name is Wayne,
Says it's boring in the middle lane,
And asks me to go up to eighty,
I turn to him and say, 'Look, matey,

You're a middle laner,
You were born to the middle lane,
And every time you doubt it,
Just sing the old refrain…'

Oh, I'm a middle laner,
I love the middle lane!
I simply won't move over
In sunshine or in rain.

I go right down the middle
From Edinburgh to Staines
And refuse to even contemplate
The other two empty lanes.

So you may flash your headlights
Or audibly complain
But I will never move over –
It goes against the grain.

Oh, I'm a middle laner,
I'll stay there till I die
And when they take me away in a hearse
Down the middle lane I'll fly!

Marks on the Motorway

A guide to the most common mysterious markings to be seen on the surface of the motorway

1. Long black tyre marks, often up to 100 feet long, going diagonally across the motorway and slanting off into the hard shoulder and even beyond

These always look like the remnants of some horrendous crash, as if someone had fallen asleep at the wheel and careered off to his death. That is what it is meant to look like. But of course if you fall asleep at the wheel you don't put the brakes on and skid – you just crash without creating skid marks! No, these black skid marks HAVE BEEN PAINTED ON THE ROAD BY THE POLICE to make drivers feel nervous and drive more carefully, in the same way that rumble strips are meant to make DRIVERS more cautious.

2. Little black tyre marks, often up to 10 feet long, going along the motorway for a very little way and then stopping

These are caused by rooks tyre-surfing behind lorries. The rooks hang on to the lorries at the back, standing on old tyres, and sort of ski along the road behind them. You must have often noticed lots of old black tyres lying on the verge of motorways, haven't you? With large black rooks hopping about next to them, trying to look inconspicuous? That's why. They're waiting for a slow lorry to come along, to jump on behind and tyre-surf from.

3. Yellow patches
When a lorry sheds its load, it is normally cleared up as soon as possible by a police cleansing unit, who pride themselves on being able to get anything off a roadway, from beer to quick-setting porridge oats. However, there is nothing much you can do about a load of bananas which has been squashed and worked in by a few passing wheels.

4. White stripes
On some motorways you pass over a set of irregularly spaced white strips which are sometimes close together, sometimes not so close together, and which we assume to be some sort of traffic calming system. Not so. If you saw it from the air, you would immediately recognise these white lines as giant bar-codes. All motorways are bar-coded at regular intervals. This enables passing aircraft to read the bar-code and get an exact fix on their position.

5. Glitter patches
Every time a motorway surface is renovated, the contractors have to put little strips of electronic sensors in the tarmac in case automatic motorway tolls ever come to be charged. This of course is highly confidential and is always denied, but when it rains the sensors do glimmer sightly just below the surface, especially when it has been worn slightly.

6. Parallel black marks going along the motorway
Very occasionally a small aircraft in distress, looking for somewhere

to make an emergency landing, tries to land on a motorway, on the grounds that it is the nearest thing to a runway it will ever find. Unfortunately for the pilot, he will never have encountered cars and lorries on a runway before. Actually, surveys show that up to 80% of vehicles will notice the plane trying to land and will take evasive action. The same surveys show that up to 20% will not notice the plane. That is why there are parallel black marks going along the motorway which then end abruptly.

7. A large white blob
In 1983 motorway police found an unexplained large white blob on the M4 motorway near Reading. It measured nine feet across and looked for all the world as if a giant bird had left its dropping there. Although this was clearly ridiculous, police analysis revealed that it was in fact chemically identical with bird dropping. Further calculation showed that to leave a dropping of this size, the bird would have to be at least fifty feet long, which is forty-eight feet longer than any known motorway bird. The police kept the information very quiet for a year. Then the blob reappeared. It was then noticed that it only appeared during Reading University Rag Week and had been engineered by chemistry students.

8. Four symmetrically placed indentations, only two or three inches deep, forming a square about 100 feet across, sometimes straddling both sides of the motorway
These are the landing marks of large interplanetary tourist flights from, we think, Mars, which like to land at about five a.m. for brief rest periods, at a time when the motorways are usually unoccupied. The occupants are usually allowed about ten minutes for relief, which they normally enjoy by playing Martian boules in the fast lane or writing graffiti in nearby fields (we call the resultant

patterns 'crop circles'). Martians do not spend a penny in the same way that we do; all their waste products are actually evaporated into the air through the skin, which explains why there are no lavatories on Mars, and why they all smell slightly odd.

OLD MOTORWAY SAYINGS

Washington Birtley, Burton West –
These are the places I love best.
Full of welcome, full of cheer,
Most unlike Leigh Delamere.

10 GREAT MOTORWAY FILMS

No 3.
The Land That Time Forgot

'Let's go to Cornwall!' they said. 'There are no motorways in Cornwall! Everything is as it used to be in Cornwall! It is like the 1950s, slow and leisurely! Let us go to Cornwall and have the holiday of a lifetime!'

And so they went to Cornwall, where miraculously there are no motorways and everything is as it was in the 1950s! Unfortunately this means they also have 1950s music, 1950s fashions, 1950s cooking and National Service. A grim story. Not for the faint-hearted.

MOTORWAY'S RUTHLESS RHYMES

LITTLE JOHNNY HEAD IN AIR

Little Johnny Head in Air
Didn't see the coach behind him,
Bits of his car went everywhere
Now it's very hard to find him.

The Art of Overtaking

As I go down the motorway
To Weston-Super-Mare
Or Cardiff, or to Swansea,
Or Bath, or anywhere,

I sometimes get the feeling,
As down the road I roar,
That everything that 's happening
Has happened to me before.

It doesn't really matter
If it's M4 or M2 –
I always get this feeling
Of definite *déjà vu.*

A strange, disturbing feeling,
Impossible to explain,
That things which once have
    happened
Are happening again.

It's not the motorway scenery
Which always seems the same,
It's not the signs or bridge design
Or the countryside I blame.

Oh no! I point the finger
At a rat-faced little man
Who sits upright at the steering
    wheel
Of an off-white little van.

I first overtook that vehicle
Nearly an hour ago
And then he overtook me,
Though I wasn't going slow.

And then I overtook him
And then he came past me,
And now we pass each other
Fairly regularly.

Every time I waken
From my motorway reverie
If I'm not overtaking him
He's overtaking me.

I seem to go no faster
Or slower, come to that,
So how on earth does he pass me,
The dirty little rat?

Every time I pass him
I leave him well behind,
And then, five minutes later,
What do you think I find?

A scruffy little vehicle
With muddy marks and dents
Overtaking my limo!
It simply doesn't make sense...

I never see him look at me
And he never catches my eye,
But we know each other well by
    now
As we pass each other by.

I've seen that man in his little van
On the road to Avonmouth.
And I've also seen him going past
On the M2, heading south.

I've seen him coming on at Leeds
And off on the Reading road,
And I fancy once I saw him,
Near Plymouth, being towed,

I've seen him in the Midlands
Going towards Liverpool
And I've passed him up in Scotland
Heading for Ultima Thule.

Oh, life is like a roulette wheel.
And what goes round, comes back,
And the thing that comes most often
Is a van with a bit of sack

Tying together the handles
On the door which no longer works,
And I know I've seen that van
    before
Elsewhere, in other circs.

And it's starting to drive me crazy
Seeing that little white van
Creeping up in my mirror
Going as fast as he can.

And my only consolation
In my haunted misery
Is that, if I'm sick of him,
He must hate the sight of me!

A Motorway Ghost Story

Jack Standish was trying to get a lift back home. Or at least part of the way home, because he had two hundred miles to go and he was unlikely to find a car going past his door. The reason he was so far from home was that he had just finished his first term at university and when choosing a university he had deliberately picked a place to go to a long way from home. This was good insofar as it got him away from the old surroundings, that is to say, his parents. But it was bad insofar as at the end of term it was a long way to go, especially if you were broke.

That is why he was now standing at the entrance to the motorway, holding up a card saying LONDON. He had thought long and hard about the wording on the card. At first he had thought he might simply put GOING HOME. Then he thought he might put, GEOGRAPHY STUDENT ABLE TO CONVERSE GRIPPINGLY FOR HOURS OR SHUT UP IF NECESSARY. Then he thought that LONDON was the correct solution if he really wanted to get a lift.

It hadn't worked so far. After thirty minutes he had had a cheery wave from a lorry already full of hitchers and that was it.

It was then that the red sports car arrived.

Arrived but didn't stop.

As he stood by the top of the slip road holding his card saying **LONDON**, the red sports car came roaring round the roundabout and seemed to come right at him, taking the entrance into the slip road badly. He didn't have time to jump. He closed his eyes.

When he opened them, the car had gone. Just missed him, presumably. God, *he* hadn't expected hitching to be dangerous as well!

'That was close,' said a voice.

He looked round. A farmer was looking out of his Land Rover, having pulled up just behind him.

'Saw it happen,' said the farmer. 'Bloody fool. Want a lift?'

'You're not going to London?' asked Jack.

'Correct,' said the farmer. 'But I'm going that way. I could drop you at the next exit, or at the service area down the road. Service area probably be better. More people stop there.'

'Thanks,' said Jack. 'Very kind.'

He listened to the farmer natter as he drove down the M. It's part of the duty of hitch-hiking: listening or talking. If the driver wants to talk, it's your job to listen. If he wants to be amused, you've got to talk. If he likes silence, you've got to shut up. If he wants to play heavy metal tapes, you'd best get out and look for another lift. But all the farmer wanted to do was talk.

'My Dad used to own a lot of this land,' he said, nodding at the fields. 'Big farm, he had. Had to sell a lot. And some got taken.'

'Taken?' said Jack. 'What for?'

'Not exactly taken,' said the farmer, 'but when they built the new service area they wanted our land for it. Dad was dead by then, so I sold it to them. Made quite a packet. Helped me buy this Land Rover...'

Minutes later the farmer dropped Jack in front of the main

entrance of the Charlminster Service Area, which was one he hadn't heard of before. He said thanks to the farmer and wandered up to the RAC man at the entrance. There was always an RAC man at the entrance to service areas. Never AA men. Perhaps the AA didn't want any more members. Perhaps they had enough on their plate. Perhaps they felt sorry for the RAC…

'Excuse me…' he said

'You want to join the RAC?' asked the man, eagerly. 'No problem!'

Jack almost laughed at the man's eagerness. He had a bristling moustache, like a World War II RAF officer's, and it seemed to stand to attention as he spoke.

'There is a problem, I'm afraid,' he said, 'I haven't got a car.'

'Never mind, sir,' said the keen RAC man. 'You could always join the RAC now and get the car later. Be nice to have a few pedestrians in!'

'No,' said Jack. 'I just wanted to know where people hitched from here, or where you think the best place to stand would be.'

'Hitch-hiking, eh?' said the officer. 'Is that how you got here?'

'Yes,' said Jack. 'Got a lift at the last exit. Interesting bloke. Local farmer. Used to own the land on which this motorway service area stands.'

The RAC man looked at him very strangely. 'Are you sure, sir?'

Jack thought about this. 'Yes, I am. At least, that's what he told me.'

'Can you describe him to me?'

'Thin. Hat. Working clothes. Like a farmer. Except one funny thing. He had a red rose in his lapel.'

The RAC man looked at him long and hard. 'I assume that you're not taking the mickey out of me, sir?'

'Why should I?' asked Jack, puzzled.

'Because the man you describe died in a car crash last November.'

Jack felt himself go faint. He dimly listened to what the RAC man was saying…

'Everyone knew him round here. Often used to come in to have a cuppa. Walk the old grounds, he would say. Then one days there was a horrible crash. I was called out to help. It was him. Stuck in the wreckage. Never forget his face. Or his red rose. It was his birthday, you see. He'd had a few too many…'

Jack couldn't think straight. None of this made sense. If the farmer was dead, how could…?

'I'd pop inside and have a cup of tea if I were you,' said the RAC man, kindly. 'I don't know what's happened to you, but you look as if you need a good sit down. You're in no fit state to start hitching. Go to Country Kitchen. Try the Earl Grey. It's my favourite.'

Jack stumbled in to Country Kitchen, still trying to take in what the RAC man had said. It seemed impossible. The man in the Land Rover had seemed so alive. How could he have dreamt it…?

'Tea or coffee, love?'

Jack looked up. There was a bright-looking girl called Ellen standing behind the machines which converted good, healthy water into various kinds of sullen brown fluid. He knew she was called Ellen because she had a name tag on her chest.

'Earl Grey,' he said. 'That's what the RAC man recommended.'

There was a silence. He looked up to find her gazing at him, open-mouthed.

'You what?'

'The RAC man outside. Just been talking to him. Nice fellow, with big bristly moustache…'

The pot of hot water made a loud noise as she dropped it on the floor. Some of it must have splashed on her but she gave no sign of feeling it. She just stood there like a statue, staring at him.

'What have I said?' Jack asked, 'What's wrong with talking to an

47

RAC man?'

'Oh my God,' said the girl. 'Oh my God, oh my God…'

At least this was taking his mind off the ghostly farmer, thought Jack, which showed that it wasn't.

'We haven't got an RAC man out there,' said the girl. 'Haven't had one for six months.'

'Oh, come on!' said Jack. 'Every motorway service area has one! You can't have a service area without an RAC man recruiting people night and day. It would be against the law not to!'

'Not here,' said the girl, not laughing. 'The RAC have withdrawn their man from here after what happened at Christmas.'

'Christmas?'

'Big fellow called Bob. Bristly moustache. Wore his hat at a jaunty angle.'

Jack nodded. He was still wearing it at a jaunty angle.

'Set upon by a gang of Hell's Angels. All drunk. Beaten up. Died in hospital…'

Jack felt he was sitting in the middle of a nightmare. None of it made sense. How could…? He turned and ran outside. He felt faint. He felt that things were getting out of control. He felt that if he didn't get away soon he might go mad. He ran to the filling station area and into the shop.

'You alright, sir?' said the assistant, cheerily. 'You look as if you've seen a ghost.'

Jack wondered what to say, how much to say, without looking crazy. 'Well,' he said, 'I've just been talking to a girl serving in Country Kitchen, a Scottish girl…'

'I don't think so,' said the petrol salesperson.

'Why not?' said Jack.

'No Scottish people working in there. They're a bit superstitious about that. Ever since…'

48

'Since what?'

'Since the terrible accident involving Ellen. She...'

Jack screamed and ran out. The first driver he came to taking petrol he begged for a lift, anywhere, just to the next service area, next exit, anywhere, please, please, please...

'All right,' said Mrs Robinson, surprised but not alarmed. He seemed a nice boy. He didn't say much, partly because he was feeling very tired, confused and faint by now, and then she dropped him at the next service area where he went to make a phone call home. He didn't have the right change. He went to the cafeteria to get some. They wouldn't give him any change. They said he had to buy something, even if only a cup of tea.

'I had a cup of tea at the last service area,' said Jack. 'Charlminster. Don't want another one.'

'Where?' asked the saleslady.

'Charlminster.'

'Never heard of it.'

'That's what it was called.'

'Never heard of it. Jenny, you ever heard of a service area called Charlminster?' This to an older woman at the next till. Jenny gave out some change to a customer, and then thought a while.

'Charlminster's about twenty-five miles back,' she said.

'Service area?'

'No, small village. There was going to be a service area there, I remember that. They planned it and everything – in fact, they planned it even before they built this one.'

'Why didn't they build it?'

'Can't remember now. Some tragedy happened. I think there was some terrible accident when they were surveying the ground – workmen killed or something – and they finally never did build it there.'

Jack had been feeling faint and unworldly until now. Now he felt as if he was in a living nightmare. Slowly he felt consciousness ebb away from him, and then he was falling, falling into a black hole...

The next day, at Charlminster Motorway Service Area, Ellen the Scots girl came out during her morning break to have a chat with Bob, the RAC man. He was already busy talking to that farmer fellow who kept dropping by. They were looking at a newspaper together.

'It's him all right,' said the farmer.

'It certainly is,' said Bob.

Ellen looked over their shoulders. There was a picture of Jack Standish, though she didn't know that that was his name. The headline said STUDENT IN HIT AND RUN TRAGEDY.

'Run over by a red sports car at the roundabout,' said Bob thoughtfully. 'Just down the road. He was hitching there.'

'So it actually happened *before* we saw him,' said the farmer.

'Och, that's impossible,' said Ellen, 'I saw him too! He was fine.'

'No, he wasn't,' said the farmer. 'He seemed ... half not there at all to me.'

'He must have been desperate to get home,' said Bob. 'So desperate that even when he died, his spirit kept going...'

'That's impossible,' said Ellen.

Do YOU think it's impossible? If yes, phone YES. If not, phone NO. If you refuse to believe in phone polls, don't phone at all...

10 GREAT MOTORWAY FILMS

No 4.
Crash

The controversial film that tried to make a link between sex and bankruptcy.

'I just get a kick out of seeing firms slide over the edge into liquidation,' says creepy leading figure Oscar to his girlfriend as he pores evilly over the balance sheet of Hard Shoulder. Hard Shoulder is a once-mighty motorway construction company which is now past its best. Within weeks Oscar has joined the company with the sole intention of gratifying his own dark desires by sabotaging its painful climb back to solvency.

The climactic scenes – as Hard Shoulder's accountants flee the country with creditors baying on their trail and Oscar is driven by the sight to heights of sexual passion – are so strong that they are only allowed to be seen in a few parts of Britain.

A Grand Motorway Quiz

★ The reason that the Eurotunnel is a rail tunnel, not a road tunnel, is that although originally it was going to be a drive-through tunnel, the French and British governments couldn't agree on which side of the road people should drive between England and France, so they made it a rail tunnel instead. True or false?

★ Who is the patron saint of motorways? (A clue: it is *not* St Christopher. St Christopher is the patron saint of travellers who try to cross motorways on foot.)

★ Which well-known motorway service area can boast all three of the following?
a) a private chapel

b) a full-time resident psychiatrist

c) an open space at the back which is licensed for the fighting of duels?

★ Can the manager of a motorway service area solemnise the marriage of two people, like the captain of a ship can?

★ If your answer to that one was No, think again for a moment. What would happen if a service area was cut off from the rest of the world by appalling floods, snow and blizzards? Suppose that among the few people trapped overnight in the service area was a young couple who were going to be married in a few weeks time, and the woman had an incurable disease and only weeks to live?

★ And the ordeal at the service area weakened her until it was obvious she had only a few *hours* to live?

★ And they both came to you, as the manager of the service area, and said: 'Please marry us while we have the chance?'

★ What then, eh? Would you refuse their heartfelt request, knowing that she might die any moment?

★ And that if she did, would he then come to you and ask you to perform the burial ceremony?

★ And are you empowered to officiate at that?

★ Well, then.

★ Which crop is most commonly grown to give green ground cover to the banks lining motorway cuttings?
a) grass
b) ground elder
c) cannabis?

★ Who was Charnock Richard?

★ It is illegal to leave coloured objects flapping or flying loose from a car window, a regulation that was obviously brought in to help stop football supporters fly club scarves out of their cars on a match day. However, as the Parliamentary draughtsman who helped frame the law was a West Ham supporter, the two colours that were omitted from the list of banned colours just happened to be the colours worn by West Ham, i.e. burgundy and that nasty grey-blue colour.

Therefore West Ham are legally the only fans who can fly their colours on the motorway. True or false?

 You are driving along the M25 when you encounter a completely stationary jam extending at least two miles in front of you. You sit in it for about half an hour, during which time it has moved perhaps a quarter of a mile. You are in danger of being late for an appointment with your accountant, which is very important to you as you have just acquired proof that your accountant has been systematically cheating you for ten years of about £2,000 a year (plus VAT) and you are afraid that if you do not turn up, he may smell a rat and flee.

In your feverish anxiety you notice that next to the hard shoulder there is a disused gate into a field and that if you drive across the hard shoulder and down the gently sloping verge you would probably be able to get into the field, and, with luck, escape across it to a gate on the far side…

Moments later, with your heart in your mouth, you have crashed through the gate and are driving across the field which, although muddy and skiddy, does not prevent your progress. At the far side of the field, having checked that nobody is following you, you find a gate that leads into a tiny lane. You drive down it and are about to get on to a B Road and safety when a rather elegant horse and carriage turns into your lane from the B Road, thus blocking your path. You hoot your horn to tell the driver to go back. Angrily, he gets out and approaches you, and it is only then that you realise that you recognise him as the Duke of Edinburgh. He leans down to your open window and asks what the devil you think you're doing driving down a private lane and frightening his horse. You open your mouth to reply. But do you address him as:

a) Your Royal Highness
b) Your Majesty
c) Your Grace?

OLD MOTORWAY SAYINGS

Gretna Green, Gretna Green,
Loveliest place I've ever seen.
Hello England, Scotland goodbye,
I shall love you till I die.

Slight Delay on the Motorway

The road was icy, the fog was dense,
He drove right through the central fence.
A van was coming the other way
And that was the end, I'm sad to say.
But he woke again a moment later,
In the queue to reach The Gates of Peter.

Ahead it stretched, that endless queue,
To the end of sight and out of view.
And by the side of the waiting line,
There stood a tall, imposing sign:
'Pearly Gate widening in progress today;
God says "Sorry for any delay".'

10 GREAT MOTORWAY FILMS

No 5.
Some Like It Hot

A wacky comedy about an Indian family who take over a small shop in a motorway service area in payment of a bad debt. They use the premises to set up the first ever motorway Indian takeaway (slogan 'The Hottest Curries on the Motorway!'). One problem with an Indian takeaway on a motorway is that people have to drive at least twenty miles from home. That's too far for a takeaway. So the Indian family determine to build their own private road to the service area! And that's where their troubles start!

Motorway Nursery Rhymes

JACK AND JILL

Jack and Jill went up the hill
In the 'Slow Lorries' lane
They ran into a foreign van
And now they're both in Spain

GREAT MOTORWAY MYSTERIES

✳ No joining point of a motorway is ever called Entrance 18. Only Exit 18.

Why are there exits from motorways but never any entrances?

✳ When you come to a coned-off area of a motorway, you know that all those cones have been put there one by one.

But who put down the first, single cone and how did he do it without being killed?

✳ The slow lane of the motorway, commonly referred to as the inside lane, is not on the inside at all but on the outside of the motorway. Conversely, the so-called outside lane is right at the very middle of the motorway next to the central reservation and should really be called the inside lane.

Why have we got the names back to front?

★ The motorway people often express their regret for things, on signs such as 'Sorry For Any Delay'.

Why do they never express their happiness, as in 'Glad All Those Cones Have Gone, Eh?'

★ The quietest part of any motorway service area is the part where the telephones are situated. The noisiest part of any motorway service area is the games arcade. In many motorway service areas, the telephone section has been put bang next to the games arcade.

Whose idea was this?

★ When you have sat stationary in a traffic tailback for nearly half an hour, without knowing what has caused the obstruction, and it then begins to move, your one consolation is that you know you will sooner or later pass the cause of the hold-up and all will be explained. but you never see anything which could remotely explain the tailback.

Why do so many traffic jams have no cause?

✸ Sometimes you see burnt-out cars at the side of motorways. Yet you never actually see a car burning. Only burnt-out cars.

Is it possible that the police take burnt-out cars and leave them at the side of the motorway in order to offer drivers a possible cause of traffic hold-ups?

✸ Sometimes, driving along the motorway, you realise that there is nothing ahead of you for two hundred yards, nor is there anything behind you for two hundred yards. You are, just for a moment, in an oasis of your own.

Why can't it always be like that?

10 GREAT MOTORWAY FILMS

No 6.

All You Ever Wanted To Know About Essex But Were Too Frightened To Ask

A remake of the Woody Allen film, but with a regional touch. If you think Essex is funny, then this is the comedy film for you. If you think Essex is just the physical expression of something rather deeper and more significant, you may well be offended.

MOTORWAY'S RUTHLESS RHYMES

SALLY AND THE PETROL

Sally simply forgot to pay
When she filled her tank with gas.
The policeman shot her later that day.
And quite right too, forgetful lass!

Motorway Family Saga

'There have always been Wylcome-Breaks at Thornley Lodge, and there always will,' thundered old Elspeth Wylcome-Break, the family matriarch, at her son, Seb.

'I don't doubt it, Mother,' said Seb patiently. 'I am very happy for the family to go on living here. I have always lived here myself, and hope I always will. I hope the family stays here as well. All I am saying is that I want to go to London.'

'And what's to become of Thornley Lodge?' stormed his mother. 'You go gallivanting off to London and leave Thornley Lodge behind! You, Seb, my boy, the son and heir! It's not right!'

'Mother, I'm only going away for the weekend! I'll be back on Sunday evening!'

'What will become of the ancestral service area if anything should happen to thee, Seb, my son! You, the son and heir!'

That much was true. Thornley Lodge Motorway Service Area had been in the Wylcome-Break family for as long as there had been a motorway running past. In Seb's youth Thornley Lodge had been run by his father, old Jabez Wylcome-Break, but ever since his father's mysterious disappearance on the night of the great hurricane in 1987, Seb had been in charge. Or rather, his mother had been…

Not many people are privileged to grow up in a motorway service area, surrounded by servants and facilities. But here at Thornley Lodge, Seb had grown into boyhood in the rarefied atmosphere of a son of the motorway gentry, rushing in and out of Julie's Pantry as soon as he could walk, running races across the pedestrian bridge to the southbound side, making friends with the pert girls at the petrol pump area…

'I shall be back, Mother,' said Seb brusquely. 'My brother Hiram can run the place as well as I can till I return. Now let's hear no more of this. Oh, by the way, Mother…'

'Yes, Seb?', asked Elspeth, apprehensively.

She hoped it was not the question she dreaded hearing from his lips, though she knew he would ask it one day. The question about his father's disappearance. But it was not to be. Not yet.

'I came across my birth certificate the other day,' said Seb, 'and I noticed that I was registered under the name Seb. I always thought I was called Sebastian. Am I not?'

'No,' said Elspeth. 'We called you Seb, simply.'

'Why is that?'

'Because we always wanted a girl, your father and I,' said Elspeth. 'But we only ever had boys. So we gave you the name we would have given you if you had been a girl. But back to front.'

'Back to front?' asked Seb, wonderingly… 'You mean that if I had been a girl I would have been called … Bess?'

'That's right.'

'And my brother Hiram?'

'Mary.'

'And Len?'

'Nell.'

Seb fell silent. Then he kissed his mother on her forehead, saying, 'I shall be back soon, Mother.'

And so he was. But not quite as soon as he expected. For during his weekend in London he met and fell in love with a girl called Sarah. And he stayed longer in London than he said he would otherwise have done because Sarah said she loved him too. And one day (the following Tuesday, actually) she said she would like to take him home to meet her parents, Mr and Mrs Rhode-Chef.

'Rhode-Chef?' asked Seb, wonderingly. 'You are a Rhode-Chef?'

'Why, yes, sirree,' said Sarah brightly. 'Perhaps I should have told you earlier, but I didn't want to seem boastful. My family have lived at the ancestral motorway service area of Dawnford Yates since the dawn of time.'

'I know,' said Seb dully.

The service area of Dawnford Yates, stood twenty miles down the motorway from Thornley Lodge. Once, many years ago, the Wylcome-Breaks had talked to the Rhode-Chefs and the Rhode-Chefs had talked to the Wylcome-Breaks, but then a disastrous vendetta had developed between the two families that nobody could quite remember the reason for. Perhaps the Wylcome-Breaks had unfairly lowered the price of their four-star petrol. Perhaps the Rhode-Chefs had made their cafeteria more attractive by wiping the tables and removing the dirty crockery. Whatever it was, it had led to a break between the two mighty families which had never been healed.

'I know,' repeated Seb, not dully but interestingly this time. 'My name is Seb ... Wylcome-Break.'

Sarah gasped. It suited her. She looked good while gasping. She did it again. Later the two of them set off for an overnight stay at Dawnford Yates, her ancestral home.

'Do you have brothers?' asked Seb.

'No, alas,' said Sarah. 'My parents always wanted boys but only got girls. I was to have been a boy and in fact I was given the boy's name I would have received, but back to front.'

'You mean…?'

'Harris,' said Sarah.

'That doesn't quite work,' said Seb.

'Of course, I was never called Sarah. I was always called Sally,' said Sarah. 'Which is Elias backwards. More or less …'

They drove past Thornley Lodge, with Seb hiding his face just in case his mother should see him go past, and arrived at Dawnford Yates in time for tea and doughnuts, 15% off, special Thursday offer.

'It may be just a wonderfully situated and equipped service area to you, but to me it's home,' whispered Sarah as they entered the portals of Dawnford Yates, past the signs saying Cars This Way, Lorries That Way, Fuel T'Other Way…

'Actually, it looks pretty much the same as Thornley Lodge,' said Seb, 'except that you've got better flowers. In fact, you've even got a gardener,' he added, pointing to an old man bent among the fuchsias.

'Old Jay?' said Sarah. 'Yes, we're lucky to have him. He came from nowhere twelve years ago, a bit like the chap in the film, the one played by Peter Sellers…'

'Inspector Clouseau?' said Seb.

'No, no, no! The one where he plays a gardener who becomes President of the USA. Anyway, Jay is just like him…'

'Your gardener is going to become the American President?' asked Seb, peering at the old man curiously.

'Never mind.' said Sarah. She stopped the car and spoke to the old man. 'Afternoon, Jay.'

'Afternoon, Miss Sarah. Welcome back to Dawnford Yates. Nice to see you back from the big city. Brought a young man back with you,

I see.'

'Yes,' said Sarah, blushing behind her dark glasses. 'This is Seb...'

She was cut off mid-sentence by a loud cry. The old gardener had fainted.

But before he had fainted and fallen into his own bed of roses, he had clearly uttered the cry: 'My son!'

Yes, dear reader, you have guessed it. When old Jabez Wylcome-Break left Thornley Lodge, it was not because of passion, an illicit love or to escape debts – it was simply to get away from his wife, Elspeth.

He knew there was one place in the world she would never look for him.
At Dawnford Yates, hated seat of rival motorway dynasty Rhode-Chef.
Especially not in the flower beds.

The rest of the story unfolds as you might expect.

Seb finally marries Sarah and unites the two dynasties, starting a new family tree of Wylcome-Break-Rhode-Chefs. Seb's mother has a welcome heart attack and dies, thus enabling old Jabez to move back to Thornley Lodge, together with his young girlfriend that nobody knows about, Maria 'Green Fingers' Tomelty, the under-gardener at Dawnford Yates.

Seb and Sarah have several children, to all of whom they give names that spell exactly the same backwards as forwards (Otto, Bob, Nan, etc.)

Fed up with planting flower beds, old Jabez introduces vegetable gardening to Thornley Lodge and pretty soon it becomes the only service area on the motorway with its own organic farm supplying meat and veg to its cafeteria.

Later, Hiram marries Ursula, power-crazy daughter of the all-powerful Granada-Forte-Something family, who have plans to open a nationwide chain of organic service areas, thus sparking off another bitter dynastic battle. But that's a story for another day...

NOT A MILE MORE, NOT A MILE LESS

A Short Story by
G. ARCHER

Amanda Croft was very beautiful. More than that, she was very, very beautiful. Actually, she was incredibly beautiful. When men passed her in the street, she turned to look at them… Sorry. The other way round. When she passed, men in the street turned to look at her. She was that beautiful.

Sometimes they were so distracted that they walked into lampposts. Often, they would get black eyes from walking into lampposts after turning to look at the beauty of Amanda Croft. Their friends would say to them, 'Hello, old boy, how did you get that black eye?' and they would say, 'I got that black eye all because of Amanda Croft', which was true, but not in the sense in which it was taken.

(This is a joke which I thought up all by myself, which is one in the eye for people who say that G. Archer never puts any jokes in his novels.)

So, anyway, Amanda Croft was very lovely, so lovely that when she passed lampposts in the street, they … Yes, well, I think you get the idea of how lovely she was.

She was also very rich. Amanda Croft was very lovely and very rich. She had lots of money. She had inherited this money from her father. Her father had the money first, then he died, then she had all the money Daddy had left over. This is called inheriting. How did Daddy get so rich ? He was a drinks tycoon. How did he die? He died in mysterious circumstances. (This may come in useful later in the book.)

One day, Amanda Croft was driving down the motorway. Maybe she was driving up the motorway. I am not sure if there is any difference between driving 'down' a motorway and driving 'up' a motorway. I will get a researcher to find this out later. She was driving a small Renault, which may come as a surprise to those of you who expect my characters to have large, posh cars, and indeed it comes as a surprise to me as well, but Amanda Croft always said that it wasn't speed that mattered, it was fitting into a parking space when you got to the other end.

Anyway, the important thing is that she was driving along the motorway, followed by her estranged husband, Douglas Croft. Douglas Croft was one of the greatest art experts in the world. When he walked along the street, nobody turned round to look at him but he could tell you exactly how much each lamppost was worth. When Amanda met him, she was carried away by his power and his knowledge, and she married him, and had two children called ****** and ******** (I have not thought of names for them yet) but now she was fed up with him and wanted a divorce. She also wanted to get remarried to Norman Longriff, the new Chancellor of the

Exchequer, with whom she was exquisitely and radiantly in love.

What she didn't know was that Douglas Croft, although he knew everything about art, had run into money troubles due to his secret gambling and now owed over £2,000,000. He needed to get the money very quickly. Of course, he could easily have sat down and written a novel and made that sort of money, but there was, as it happens, an even easier way of making a large amount of ready cash, and that was by laying his hands on Amanda's fortune. They were not yet divorced, and if Amanda were to die first, in a motorway accident for instance…

That was why Douglas Croft was driving up the motorway with murderous intent. What he didn't know was that Norman Longriff, Chancellor of the Exchequer, was aware of what Douglas Croft was up to, and was driving right behind him.

One, two, three. Amanda, Douglas, Norman.

What none of them realised was that round the next bend there was the most almighty motorway pile-up.

One after the other they went into it. None of them survived.

Which was just as well, as I couldn't think what was going to happen next.

Flying Down the Motorway

One day I rose before the dawn
  While frost was still upon the lawn
   I put an extra jersey on
      (The temperature was minus 1)
       Then jumped into my Ford Granada
          And revved her up till, full of ardour,
             Off we sped towards old Purley
             And hit the motorway so early
          That we were alone on the M25 –
       It could have been our private drive!
      While other motorists were abed
    Me and my Ford Granada sped
  Down that enchanted silver road
Where normally the traffic slowed.
I tell you, pushing 95
  At four a.m., we came alive!
    I hurtled down the outer lane
      In not so much a car as a plane,
        Cleared for take-off, in the dawn,
         Straining hard to be airborne,
           Just me and my trusty Ford Granada
           Taking off like Douglas Bader…!
        For a while I seemed to fly,

Streaking round the London sky,
Racing round the great blue yonder,
Shooting down a helpless Honda,
Getting Fiats in my sights,
Downing Saabs in open fights,
Knocking out a wounded Lada
With my mighty Ford Granada…!
Dawn raid done, and hungry now,
I started looking for some chow
And ended up at old South Mimms,
Downing bacon, eggs and Pimms…

Motorway Nursery Rhymes

I SPY

I spy
With my little eye
Something nasty going past.
Oh, it's a man
With a caravan
Overtaking far too fast

The Sad Song of the Man Who Left His Wife Behind

Oh listen, you motorway drivers, to me,
and next time you stop at the WC,
Make sure that you don't leave the key in the car
And when you come back, find your car is afar.

I was only away for a minute or two,
But when I got back from the motorway loo,
The space where my second-hand Bentley had been
Was filled by a cheap British Leyland machine.

Oh, where is my Bentley, the love of my life?
And where, come to think, is my good lady wife?
She went off, they told me, a moment ago
With your car and a sales rep whose first name was Joe.

So next time you stop on the M for a pee,
Don't trust your companion alone with the key.
Take all the keys with you before you begin,
And if it's a Bentley, then lock your wife in!

How a Motorway is Named

● ●

PART II

A new motorway has to be given its name at a small ceremony lasting no more than five or ten minutes, which makes its name legally enforceable and watertight.

The wording of the ceremony goes as follows.

'Who giveth this motorway its name?'

'I do.'

'Are you the Man from the Ministry?'

'Yes.'

'The MOT?'

'We don't call it that any more. It's now called the Department.'

'But you are the man from the department?'

'Oh, yes.'

'And what name do you give this motorway?'

'The M16.'

'If there be any present who see any hindrance in the naming of this motorway the M16, or who knows of any other motorway already called the M16, let him now make his objection known or be henceforth silent.'

There being no objection, the officiator shall then say: 'Dearly beloved, building motorways is a natural institution, ordained of God, created so that two great urban areas can be joined together in commercial closeness…'

And the congregation shall say: 'Yes, all right, get on with it! We have got an official reception to get to and the champagne won't stay sparkling all day!'

And the officiator shall say: 'All right, all right, keep your hair on!'

And putting on his symbolic hard hat, and taking up his symbolic theodolite, he shall shatter the symbolic bottle of cheap bubbly against the bridge and shall say: 'I name this motorway the M16, and I now declare it closed for repairs for several weeks. The Department apologises for any inconvenience caused.'

Motorway Nursery Rhymes

JACK AND JILL

Jack and Jill went up the hill
Much faster than they oughter
And they've gone and lost their licence
For another year and a quarter

The Wonderful World *of* Motorway Nature

Nature on the motorway is very special because most of the wild things you will see on your motorway journey will not occur in any other habitat.

You see, the motorway is a very dangerous place to live, so that any wild thing that chooses the motorway to live must be either very brave or, more likely, very stupid.

Not only that, but motorway nature is bound together in a series of tight ecological links which means that all motorway species depend very closely on one another.

Here is how it works.

We will start with the most familiar sight that motorway nature provides, the Motorway Bird of Prey.

Up in the air beyond the hard shoulder it hovers, fluttering endlessly. And as the cars go by, you can hear the passengers saying: 'Gosh, children, look at that bird of prey! It is hovering there with its eyes glued on the field looking for mice or a baby rabbit, and when it sees its prey, it will *swoop* down and eat it!'

But the passengers are wrong. The Motorway Bird of Prey is not looking for live prey at all. After all, you have often seen the Bird of Prey hovering, but how often have you seen it swoop on its prey?

Never!

That is because the Motorway Bird of Prey is waiting for you, the motorist, to run something over which he can then carry off and eat at his leisure.

What he is hoping you will run over is the Hapless Hedgehog. The Hapless Hedgehog is so called because however often he sets out from one side of the motorway to get to the other, he never makes it. You'd think he'd learn, wouldn't you? Or at least cross at the dead of night when he's got a fighting chance, but oh no – he never learns.

Of course, not all hedgehogs try to cross the motorway. Some are quite happy to stay where they are and never leave home. It is only the more adventurous and enterprising ones that try to get across the motorway. And get killed. What this means is that all the boring, unadventurous hedgehogs are surviving and all the go-ahead ones are dying out. In terms of evolution, this means that we are breeding a race of nervous, dull hedgehogs.

However, the Motorway Bird of Prey never actually gets to eat the Hapless Hedgehog which you have so kindly prepared for him. That is because the Hard Shoulder Bird gets there first. This is a large, black bird, not unlike a rook or crow. It hops around the hard shoulder all day long among the bits of old black tyre discarded by lorry drivers who simply can't be bothered to take them home after a blow-out and massive motorway pile-up. For a long time people thought that the Hard Shoulder Bird might actually feed off the tyres, but now we realise that they get to the Hapless Hedgehog before the Bird of Prey does. Nobody, incidentally, has ever seen one actually in flight, and it is not certain if the Hard Shoulder Bird can actually fly or not.

Meanwhile, on days when hedgehogs are not on the run, the birds feed off Motorway Worms and other small creatures too small for the motorist to see which also attempt to cross the motorway. It must be a terrifying sight for a worm as he sets out across what to him is an desert of blackness with the occasional killer car whizzing past. It must be like those scenes in science fiction films when the hero is flying somewhere deep in outer space with rogue planets, runaway asteroids and hostile fighters from the Planet Glunt trying to finish you off. No wonder many worms and other small creatures make their homes in the central reservation when they reach it and never try to complete the crossing, which may explain the old joke.*

The reason that so many animals try to make the crossing, apart from stupidity, is that they have been eating one of the plants found only on the hard shoulder, Motorway Marijuana. This is almost always found growing behind the lay-bys marked 'Patrol Vehicles Only'. Nobody knows for sure if the marijuana is planted there by people who reckon that it is the last place the police will look, or by the police themselves for their own private pleasure and profit, but that is where you will find this halluci-

---

Old joke. One worm is about to cross the motorway when he sees another worm over on the central reservation. Terrified by the prospect of braving the traffic, he shouts: 'How did you get there?' The other worm shouts back: 'I didn't. I was born here!'

78

natory weed which has such an amazing effect on creatures who eat it.

This brings us full circle back to the Motorway Bird of Prey who also feeds off the Motorway Worm, and is completely unaware that he is eating a creepy-crawly thing full of half-digested marijuana. This, according to some ornithologists, is why the Motorway Bird of Prey hovers all day long without swooping. He is stoned, and is watching the cars go by, saying to himself: 'Wow! Fantastic! There goes another! And another ... Wow...!'

Motorway Nursery Rhymes

HEY DIDDLE DIDDLE

Hey diddle diddle
Drive down the middle
Out for a Sunday ride
And you will be overtaken
By cars on either side

10 GREAT MOTORWAY FILMS

No 7.
The Birds

Where did they come from, those birds ? Those frightening black birds that hopped around at the edge of the motorway? Big, black birds that seemed to be eating old bits of tyre? And where did those birds come from that hovered over the motorway, like birds of prey waiting to swoop on their quarry? Except that these birds *never swooped on their prey*, but just hovered over the motorway, waiting, waiting for something?

What were they all waiting for?

Then one day a motorist stranded on the hard shoulder was attacked by the birds. Black birds. Hawk-beaked birds. Pecking, pecking.

By the time the rescue vehicle got there, he was dead.

The terror had begun.

BAD BREATH

A Moral
Motorway Story

It was rather odd that Bill Blunkett should worry about having bad breath, as he had taken so many other precautions about his personal hygiene. He had eliminated dandruff from his head and shoulders, he had made sure that his nasal hair was trimmed with military precision and he had even mastered the golden rule of after-shave lotion.

(The golden rule of after shave lotion, if you are interested, is that putting too much on is worse than putting none on, and that if all those men who go round smelling like an explosion in a perfume factory realised how they spread asphyxiation, the after-shave lotion industry would plummet.)

But still Bill Blunkett worried that he might have bad breath. This was because he had once read that you can never smell your own breath, in the same way that you can never hear your own snoring or see yourself from behind. You are so used to your own smell that it cannot impinge on you, and therefore everyone who has bad breath thinks he has acceptable breath. The same is true of people who have acceptable breath. So you never know if you have bad breath or not.

Bill Blunkett sometimes tried breathing into his cupped hand and then sniffing quickly to see if he could catch the odour of his own respiration. It was useless. All he could smell was the warm, slightly sweaty smell of his own hand. This was all done in strict privacy, of course, as indeed was the experiment when he breathed into a paper bag and sealed it up, then later had a sniff.

It smelt of paper bag. Which is what you would expect if you had bad breath to which you were already accustomed.

It drove Bill Blunkett barmy.

There was nobody he could ask. He had a wife and two children, of course, and several score colleagues, but they were precisely the people who would have to put up with his bad breath (if he had it) and who could not be trusted to give an honest or unmalicious answer.

He could see the dialogue in advance.

Him: 'Darling, do I ever have bad breath?'

She: 'No, not really. Except when you have been drinking, or eating, or smoking, or chewing gum…'

Or perhaps more like this…

Him: 'Darling, do I ever have bad breath?'

She: 'Never mind about that – have you booked the car in for its service yet?'

There are some things you can never consult intimate friends and relations about – such things as sexual problems, table manners, the technique of tying a bow-tie, simple spellings and how to drive better – and bad breath is one of these. Far better to consult a complete stranger. And that is exactly what Bill Blunkett did.

He had stopped one day for a cup of tea on the motorway and had sat down at a table already occupied by a tall, dark respectable-looking stranger. With a courage he hardly knew he possessed, he leant forward and addressed the stranger.

'May I ask you a favour? Does my breath smell?'

He breathed over him.

'Not specially,' said the man, and rose to leave almost immediately afterwards.

The quality of Bill Blunkett's life soared after that motorway encounter. He had it on unimpeachable, unbiased authority that his breath was OK! A completely impartial arbiter had told him that halitosis was not a danger! You should have seen his social poise increase and his courage at parties and dinners take him through previously uncharted waters.

It even affected his work. His increased confidence gave him a more dynamic attitude and he soon won promotion, and was relocated to a senior position in Yorkshire.

The first day he encountered his new boss, he thought he recognised him. So did his new boss.

'My God,' said his new boss, without thinking. 'It's the man on the motorway with the horrible breath!'

It was at this point that Bill Blunkett's life took a decided downturn again.

Motorway Nursery Rhymes

HALF A POUND OF EVERTON MINTS

Half a pound of Everton mints
Half a pound of sherbert
That's the way to smell more sweet
When you breathe for PC Herbert.

Motorway Closed Ahead – and Behind!

As I was going to Scarborough Fair
I saw a signpost standing there:
'Road to Scarborough Blocked Ahead –
Why not go somewhere else instead?'

'Well, then,' I thought, 'perhaps I may
Go down the ancient Pilgrim's Way,
Follow Chaucer's merry crew
At high speed down the old M2!'

But when I motored down to Kent
I saw to my astonishment
A sign saying 'Pilgrims, Stop! No way!
You can't come here! We're closed today!'

Well, call me stubborn, call me proud,
But all at once I said out loud:
'I will not give up easily!
There must be somewhere open to me!

I'll drive across this pleasant land
For my day off, as I have planned,
Until I find an amenity,
Which is open, and which is free!

I know! I'll drive to Wenlock Edge
To see the primrose in the hedge,
The baby lamb, the new-born goat
Just as A. E. Housman wrote!'

And so I jumped into my car
(Though Shropshire really is quite far)
And drove along the motorway
(Past signs all saying 'Closed Today')

Until I saw to my chagrin
A signpost standing somewhere in
The High Street in Much Wenlock town:
'Sorry – Wenlock Edge closed down'!

I stopped a friendly AA man
And said to him politely, 'Can
You tell me what's ado?
Why is everywhere shut, and who

Is ultimately the man we thank?'
The AA man said: 'Barings Bank.
They have got all this in trust!
Now the buggers have gone bust!'

Did you know it is against the Law NOT to have the following objects in your car, clearly visible or, preferably, hidden?

✓ An empty box of tissues

✓ One boot

✓ A ball

✓ A road atlas of Britain, published no later than 1988, with the pages bent over at the corners so that you can now neither see the roads at the edge or the page numbers

✓ A dog lead, nearly bitten through

✓ Twelve tapes, of which one must be Status Quo and another an audio book featuring Martin Jarvis

✓ One bottle of water (empty)

✓ One newspaper, with headline half-visible saying '...In New Tory Scandal', and a three-month-old crossword still not completed

✓ One petrol can (empty)

✓ One carton apple juice (full, but out of date)

✓ A pair of sun glasses

✓ A video rental box (empty) which you keep meaning to take back to the video shop to house the video which you have already taken back some time ago

✓ Five 2p pieces

✓ Between two and six pieces of car-trim which have become detached from the car during the last six months and which you are unwilling to throw away in case they can reattach them at the next service and which are now knocking around in the car getting so battered it is unlikely this will ever happen

✓ Ditto, a bolt, two nuts and a screw

✓ An apple core, very brown, very dry

✓ A boiled sweet, flavour doubtful even when first unwrapped, original colour red or perhaps blue, half-sucked and subsequently abandoned and now sticking with great tenacity to the under side of the back seat

✓ Wrapping of above

✓ Or perhaps of some other sweet

✓ The magazine belonging to some now defunct Sunday newspaper

✓ Something that looks like a £1 coin but always turns out on inspection to be one of the least valuable French coins

✓ A rolled up Sainsbury receipt

✓ A small wild flower belonging to a bunch which was fresh and colourful when you picked it but had gone all limp by the time you got home. Still, you put them in water anyway and tried to revive them, all except this one which you accidentally dropped in the car and which never even made it to the house

✓ What looks like sawdust but is actually potato crisps reduced to a fine dust by the feet of small children

10 GREAT MOTORWAY FILMS

No 8.
North By Northwest

He went north. He crossed the border. He kept heading north. He passed Glasgow. He kept heading north by northwest, as he had been instructed to do. And then it struck him. There were no more motorways! So that was why traffic was coming towards him on his side of the road! It was their side as well! Just as he realised it, he was hit by the car.

He woke up in hospital.

'You'll have to get well soon,' they said. 'We're closing this hospital down this afternoon.'

The Chauffeur Blues

Falling asleep on the motorway
Is the quickest way to die, they say.
Well, I've been sleeping for many a year
And I think you'll agree that I'm still here.
So I'll tell you how to avoid a crash –
Just be like me and have plenty of cash!
For what I do when I get on the M
Is pay someone else for the driving game.
I go to my car and get in the back
And say to my Chauffeur, name of Jack:
'Home, Jack, please and cut out the chat;
There's nothing keeps me awake like that.'
And I lean right back and take a kip,

Which normally lasts till the end of the trip.
And I may look a right old toff
As I loll in the back and doze right off,
But I couldn't care less, if I'm fresh again,
When we turn off the M and go down my lane.
My one and only fatal mistake
Was thinking Jack could stay awake.
Last week he blinked and gave a cough
Closed his eyes and nodded off,
And we left the road and ran over a rook,
And then we hit a concrete block…
Now I sit in a hospital bed
With bandages around my head
And Jack's in bed right over there
With both his legs stuck in the air.
And when I get out, I'm going by train,
And never back on the M again.

The Ballad of the Female Hitch Hiker

'Twas at the approach to the M that I spied her,
A-holding a placard with letters so bold:
'Chemistry student, going to Sheffield,
Very good talker, twenty years old.'

She stood there so pretty, my heart gave a flutter,
So I pulled to the side, and over she walked;
She got into the car and she talked and she talked
And she talked and she talked and she talked and she talked...

Till I stopped at an exit and said to her firmly,
'I haven't the faintest what you're on about,
But I know that you give me a pain in the backside'
And I opened the door and chucked the girl out.

And now when I go up the M1 to Sheffield,
I drive with my personal placard in view:
'Marketing manager, now pushing fifty,
Happily listening to Radio Two.'

MOTORWAY ACTORS

You never know what to say to actors. If you ask them whether they're working, you could be stepping on a very sore toe. But if you don't, you could be ignoring their big break. I usually just say 'What's new?'

That's what I said when I met Sid the other day. He is an actor. He occasionally works. But he is much more often in the pub, which is where I met him the other day.

'Sid!' I said. 'Long time no see. How are things with you, darling? What's new?'

He frowned. I had forgotten that Sid is not one of your actual effusive theatre people.

'I'll rephrase that,' I said. 'Tell me, Sid, how's the world treating you?'

He kept frowning. I had also forgotten that he hates clichés. What *did* he like, then? I remembered. Pretentious foreign phrases, that's what he likes.

'Que pasa, hombre?' I said.

His brow cleared. 'Pasa nada,' he said. 'Well, that's not strictly true. I'm working. Not only that, but I'm in the middle of a long run at the moment.'

'Brilliant!' I said, highly relieved, more for my sake than his. 'Muy bueno! Where's the job?'

'Down the M4'

Could be Bath. Good. Could be the last weeks of the panto at the Bristol Hippodrome. Not so good. Could be strolling players at the Glastonbury Festival. Could be worse.

'Whereabouts down the M4?'

'Beyond Junction 12.'

'You jest,' I said, in that mock-heavy tone resorted to by British conversationalists when they can't actually think of a joke.

'I kid you not,' he said. 'I have been working on the M4 for six months. As an actor.'

Intrigued, I bought Sid a couple of rounds of drinks and heard one of the most amazing stories I have heard in years.

'The thing is, the Department of Transport have developed a penchant for public relations recently,' said Sid. 'Well, they had to, really. So many apparently healthy lanes have been coned off, and so much muttering was heard from the public, that they had to offer a bit of window dressing. That's why they started posting notices with explanations, like 'Road Mending to Replace Worn Out Surface' or 'Road Widening in Progress.'

'I see,' I said, not seeing.

'But there was still a large measure of discontent, caused mainly by people who used the motorway and could see with their very own eyes that when the motorway was reduced to two lanes, or even one, the road works area often stood silent and inactive. There is nothing much more galling than crawling past a motorway works area in some hot and sweaty jam and being able to see for yourself that absolutely nothing is being done by engineers, motorway builders or anyone.'

'Right.'

'Right. So what do you think they did?'

I thought for a moment.

'Hired some more workers?'

'Nah,' scoffed Sid. 'You don't know the DoT. No, what they did was hire some actors. Get us in to *look* like workers. An actor in a yellow hard hat looks very like a builder in a yellow hard hat, and costs half the money. Half the motorway works areas you pass are populated entirely by actors.'

'You're kidding!'

'I jest you not,' said Sid, coining a new cliché by accident. "Have you not noticed that

quite often these work areas seem to be swarming with workers, *yet not a single bit of machinery is actually being used*?'

Now that he came to mention it, he was absolutely right. I had noticed this.

'We don't always work on the same motorway,' said Sid. 'We get moved around a lot. I'm up the A1(M) next week. Of course, wherever you go it's basically the same production and the same plot and everything, if you can call it a plot, but at least you get to change parts. Next week I'm playing the part of a bullying overseer, with clipboard. It's a bit of a boring character part. But it's better than my last role, which was the part of a man fixing the generator for the night-time lighting. God, that was boring. And they gave me these awful trousers, which British workmen wear and which don't quite cover your bottom but keep slipping down. I told them, if I had known that the part involved nudity…! They said that they thought it was justified on dramatic grounds… Incidentally, this is all totally hush hush…'

I wasn't sure whether to believe Sid or not. On the whole, I thought not. But yesterday, when crawling past one of those motorway works areas I had a closer look. The workmen all looked quite authentic to me. And then my wife shook me rigid by saying: 'How strange. Did you see what was written on the front door of that white Portakabin?'

'No.'

'It said: "Green Room".'

Motorway Nursery Rhymes

THE DEATH OF RELIANT ROBIN

All the birds of the air
  Fell a-sighing and a-sobbing
When they heard of the death
  Of Reliant Robin
When they heard of the death of Reliant Robin.
  'Who saw him fail?'
  'I,' said the snail,
  'He was put up for sale,
  I saw him fail.'
  'Who saw him go?'
  'I,' said the crow,
  'When his cash wouldn't flow,
  I saw him go.'

Crisps in My Lap

A NEW MOTORWAY THRILLER

Introducing Hank Mogul, the detective who operates in the place we all know best, the motorway. But nobody knows the motorway like Hank Mogul…

Hank drew his battered Volvo Estate into the filling station at the Pork Scratchings Service Area, switched off the ignition, and walked into the little room where they take your money and hope you'll buy crisps and sweets while you're queuing.

'Fill her up,' said Hank to the cashier.

'It's self-service,' said the man, a spotty youth of about twenty whose main ambition in life was to go out and get drunk that evening. People don't have big ambitions like they used to. 'What happens is, you take your own petrol. You serve yourself and then you come in here and pay…'

Hank stared at him. The World Health Organisation has nearly eradicated smallpox, he thought. Why couldn't it do the same for acne?

'Fill her up,' he said again.

There was something about the way Hank looked at him, something about the way his eye glinted, something about the way Hank lifted him up by his bow-tie and shirt and banged his head on the ceiling, that impressed the spotty young man.

'I'll do it,' he said.

'Thank you,' said Hank.

Hank was going to need all the petrol he could get. He was going to need all the help he could get, come to that. The thing was, Hank was on the trail of an obscene telephone caller, and he didn't have much experience with obscene telephone callers.

In fact, he didn't have any experience with obscene telephone callers at all.

There are certain crimes which, in the nature of things, you don't encounter very often on motorways. Piracy is one. Cattle rustling is another. And Hank had thought that making obscene telephone calls was another. Until this bloke had turned up, this bloke who was making obscene phone calls using only the emergency phones at the side of the motorway.

The local car rescue firms were getting pretty fed up with it. Nobody knew who it was. The police didn't want to handle it. So they called in Hank Mogul to crack it, and so far he hadn't got anywhere either.

'Want me to wipe the windscreen and check the oil?' said the spotty young man sarcastically.

'Yes, please,' said Hank.

The man hesitated, then did it. When Hank came to pay, he tipped him a couple of quid.

'You've paid too much,' said the young man.

'It's called a gratuity,' said Hank. 'It goes back to the days before self-service. Ask your dad about it.'

'What do I do with it?' said the young man, fingering the two quid.

'Buy yourself a matching spotty bow-tie,' said Hank, and then he hit the road.

He settled into the slow lane, wondering as he did so why people called it the slow lane. Half the time it was more like the fast lane, as he knew you could safely do 80 or 90 mph between lorries. The police never stopped anyone for speeding in the slow lane. They probably never even noticed anyone in the slow lane. He settled gradually into the rhythm of the motorway again, the swish of the tyres, the bits of black tyre on the hard shoulder, the lorries flashing lights at each other, the children waving from the backs of coaches…

Hank found himself wondering just how this motorway phone pest worked. He probably took a risk, stopped right by the emergency phone, made his dirty phone call and sped off. Not like that poor bloke, thought Hank, as he passed a man on the hard shoulder trudging along towards him. There was nothing like the misery of the motorist who one moment had been cocooned inside his safe little spaceship and the next was cast out into outer space.

Perhaps nobody except a motorway detective like Hank Mogul would have registered unease, but two or three miles further on he became worried. Why had he become worried? Because, he realised almost subconsciously, he had not passed a broken-down car. That man he had seen trudging along the motorway could only have been walking from a broken-down car. But there was no broken-down car. Therefore the man was just walking along the motorway. But nobody walks along motorways, unless … unless he is making anonymous obscene telephone calls.

Hank suddenly wanted badly to go back and talk to that man. But you can't go back along motorways. There are rules against it. One of the rules is that you have to wait for the next exit. However, the next exit was twelve miles on. On the other hand, there was another motorway service area coming up...

Hank came off the motorway, pulled up at the filling station and went to the cashiers.

'What pump number?' asked the attendant.

The man was about forty. He had bad acne. The WHO will have to get cracking before the problem gets out of hand, thought Hank.

'Listen to me *very* carefully,' said Hank. 'I am not buying petrol. I am buying information. Every motorway service area has two methods of access. One is from the motorway itself. The other is via a secret access road to some small local B road that only the employees know about it. I want to use it. Where is it?'

'We never tell people...'

Hank pushed across a £20 note.

'It's that little track in the woods over there.'

'Thanks.'

Hank drove out by the track, hit the B road and came back to the motorway again where he spotted, among some trees, just what he had hoped he would spot – an empty parked car, of a sort that might belong to a man trudging along a hard shoulder, who might just be an obscene telephone caller.

He stopped and went over to the car. It was locked. He unlocked it. (A motorway detective has to know how to unlock cars.) Then he looked inside. He registered the fact that the owner of the car possessed more Dire Straits tapes than it seemed possible for any one man to possess but he didn't have time to register any other fact before a voice behind him said: 'Stay right where you are!'

Like to know more? Stay tuned for the next episode of 'Crisps In My Lap'! Other Hank Mogul thrillers on sale include 'Twiglets In My Turn-Ups', 'A Burning Cigarette Somewhere In My Lap' and 'An Out-Of-Control Juggernaut In My Wing Mirror'.

10
GREAT
Figures in Motorway History

1. Baron Norman de Chievelys

Born Norman Stourton, he rose through motorway administration (Lieutenant of Lorry Parks, Vice-Chairman of Verges, Head of Hard Shoulders) to achieve fame as Controller of the Cones Hot Line. This little understood service was turned by him into a popular, even mythical institution, whereby anyone who had any query, complaint or even plaudit concerning coned off areas of the motorways could phone up and complain, or query, or, well, plaudit.

'In the period of my tenure we handled well over 3,000,000 calls,' he said, 'and I am proud to say that in none of those cases did we admit liability or responsibility for anything. In almost every case we contrived to make the motorist feel that he was at fault. This was public relations at its finest.'

When he retired and the Cones Hot Line was wound up, he was raised to the peerage by a grateful John Major, though it was never very clear what he was grateful for. Stourton chose to be titled after his favourite service area: the first person ever to receive a 'motorway' title.

2. General Sir Paul de la Snookerie

The hero in 1978 of the siege of Upton Tree Service Area (no longer operating). It was the first ever armed siege on a motorway, and Sir Paul remembers it as if it were yesterday.

'It was the first armed siege on a motorway and I remember it as if it were yesterday,' says Sir Paul. "What happened was this: the day before yesterday I got word that an armed gang were holding

the staff of Julie's Pantry hostage at Upton Tree, so yesterday I got a punitive expedition together and we went in, guns blazing."

And was it a successful raid?

'Yes, today I think I can report complete success. Well, put it this way,' says Sir Paul, 'Upton Tree Service Area will never be operable again now that we've finished with it.'

For the full story of the siege and its aftermath, read Sir Paul's Book, *I Blew Up A Car Park*.

3. Sir Arthur Mallard

The Geographer Royal, and the man who first thought of colouring motorways blue on the map. The Inland Waterways people fought bitterly against this, saying that blue had always been reserved for rivers and canals, and that if motorways were coloured blue, river trade would continue to decline. They were absolutely right. Mullard was later given a knighthood by the grateful Tories, whose colour is, of course, blue.

4. Wendy Simpkins

The first person ever to be born in a motorway service area, and so far the only one. Wendy Simpkins first saw the light of day in the staff lounge at the Upton Tree Service Area (no longer operating).

Her mother, Alice, remembers it well. In the words she used when she sold her story exclusively to the *Sun* ('My Motorway Miracle Baby'):

'I simply had no idea I was even pregnant! I had just asked my husband to stop at the next service area because I had this terrible stomach ache, but the lady in the lady's toilet said, I think you're having a baby. And, do you know, she was absolutely right!'

Husband, Pete, remembers it slightly differently, as he related exclusively to the *News of the World* ('My Motorway Delivery'):

'We had planned this baby very carefully, and on the day appointed we were on our way to St Judith's Hospital, but my wife, who has never been the best map reader in the world, gave me a wrong turning on to the motorway, and then said, 'Pete, I think I'm starting to have contractions!' Well, even in an emergency it's hard to do a U turn on the M, so we pressed on to the next service area, and as luck would have it…'

Luckily, Wendy Simpkins herself was too young at the time to remember a third, different version.

5. *Hugo Barabbas*

Hugo Barabbas was the person who conceived the idea of the first massive new dictionary of modern times, the Oxford Motorway Dictionary, which would list all terms and words peculiar to motorway life, or which had different meanings on the motorway. As he used to say, "Till motorways came along, we never had anything in the language to describe tailbacks, central reservations or lorries shedding their load. It is my life's work to put it all in one book."

The first two volumes of this mighty work have already been published. The first was *A1(M) – Bollard* and the second is *Bolton Wanderers Supporters Club – Contraflow.*

6. Sheila Finestone

Sheila Finestone was the first person to become aware of the plight of people trapped overnight in their cars on motorways, or to do anything about it.

'There may be people dying in Africa,' she told the world, 'but there are people starving to death in our own country every time it snows on the M6, or if not starving at least running desperately short of rolls and Appletise.'

She formed an emergency squad of aid helpers who would appear on the scene of every appalling motorway weather disaster and fearlessly make their way to stranded motorists with rations and first aid supplies. Finestone, or the 'Lady with the Lunch Box', as she became known, was later made a baroness for her good work. She chose the title Baroness Chievelys, but it had already been taken by Norman Stourton's wife, so she reluctantly became Lady Julie's Pantry instead.

7. Dennis Masterman

Dennis Masterman is believed to be the first person officially to become a resident of a motorway. Homeless in London, he scraped together enough money to buy an old car and drove as far as the Upton Tree Service Area (no longer operating) where he took up residence in the car park, and gave out Upton Tree Service Area Car Park (North Side) as his legal address. When the authorities realised what was happening, they started to move him on from one service area to another, but he thwarted them by buying half a dozen old cars, leaving them at different areas, and moving from one to the other.

8. Lord Leigh Delamere

Lord Leigh Delamere can take the credit for the invention of motorway-twinning. Charged with the task of coming up with an idea for brightening motorway travel, he devised the notion of twinning motorways in the same way that towns are twinned. Initial doubts were dispelled when a pioneer party from an Italian autostrada came for celebrations on the M4, and the results were said to be wildly successful. The scheme is now up and running, except that nobody can find any foreign road willing to be twinned with the M25. Lord Delamere, incidentally, is not named after the well-known service area. That is his hereditary title.

9. Oscar Traill

The legendary copywriter who first invented the phrase 'Sorry For Any Delay', which has since become a standard sign everywhere. It isn't often known that 'Sorry For Any Delay' was only the final version of a slogan which different teams had been working on for months. When Traill came on the scene, the sign as it stood read: 'If you can't stand the pain, why not go by train?' Before that, previous versions had read, 'Missed Your Appointment? Too Bad,

Mate!', and 'Win Some, Lose Some'.

'Before Oscar,' said Ted Mabey (see next entry), 'it had never occurred to us to apologise for anything. Now we are working on a speed restriction sign so conciliatory that it says, "Sorry, Sir, But It's Seventy".'

10. Ted Mabey

Also known as 'The Boy from Bolton', who rose from nothing to be a famous figure on the motorways. He originally had no intention of working on the motorway system and in fact was travelling as a football supporter with a fan club from Bolton Wanderers to a fixture in London when the coach stopped off at the Upton Tree Service Area (no longer operative) and mistakenly left him behind when it resumed the trip.

'I was standing on the bridge between the north and south sides, just watching the traffic go past, when I saw our coach go under,' he says. 'So I thought I'd cut my losses and wait till they called in on the way back.'

However, they decided to come back another way and never did call in at Upton Tree. Young Ted, stranded, got a job at the service area wiping trays and stayed there. Ten years later he had risen to become manager of Upton Tree, and then began the series of innovations which made him a pioneer in service area management – Britain's first motorway bookie's shop, a lake where people could fish, the first service area licensed for weddings, the first service area with a film location bureau which sought to hire the place out for location work, etc, etc.

When he retired, he desired to be known as Lord Watford Gap, but couldn't, as he hadn't been offered a title.

PETROL PUMP PAYMENT

Mr and Mrs Meredith
And their little boy and girl
Were driving down to the coast one day,
Out for a bit of a whirl,
When Father said, 'Oh me, oh my,
We're very low on fuel!'
And so they stopped to get some more,
Which is the normal rule.

While Father filled the petrol tank
Mama bought bags of sweets
And crisps and chocolate-coated bars,
And other tasty eats,
For she got bored on long car trips
And so she sat and ate
Which helped to stave off boredom
But made her overweight.

Her children had gone off meanwhile
By themselves to find the loo,
Which, at the age of eight and ten,
They were old enough to do.
And when the sweets were purchased
And pennies had been spent
Papa switched on the engine
And said: 'OK – let's went!'

(One of those jocular phrases
Which fathers like to use
Thinking they sound quite comical,
Though no one shares their views…)
Mother took a sweetie
And the kids got belted up,
Dad revved up the engine
And said out loud: 'Hey yup!'

(Another of those phrases
Which drive you round the bend –
It's amazing that more fathers
Don't meet a violent end!)
And he left the service area
To rejoin the motorway
Totally oblivious
That he'd forgotten to pay!

Yes, stricken by amnesia
He'd offered no credit card,
Not even reached for his cheque book.
So before he'd gone a yard

The girl at the petrol counter
(The one marked 'Pumps 1–9')
Had picked up her secret telephone
And got the police on the line.

'It's Sue at Northbound Petrol
Reporting an abscondee.
A guy in a red Fiesta,
Owing £30.43.'
'OK, Susan, gotcha,
Just leave it up to us.
We'll get the money back to you –
Nae bother and nae fuss.'

And so the powerful police car
Slid out upon the road
For nothing annoys a policeman
More than when money is owed.
Meanwhile poor Mr Meredith,
Unaware of his fate,
Drove at a steady 60,
While his wife sat there and ate,

And a couple of miles behind him
A police car, flashing blue lights,
Looked for the red Fiesta
To get him bang to rights.
And the gap between them lessened
As cars got out of the way,
For when a police car flashes you,
We normally tend to obey,

And breathe a little sigh of relief
And thank our lucky stars,
As the police sweeps past, a-chasing
Some other car, not ours.
But just when Mr Meredith
Was in danger of having to stop,
Another driver, called Reggie,
Looked round and saw the cop.

Now, the car that Reg was driving
Was stolen property,
And Reggie's basic instinct
Was to step on the gas and flee.
So he went up to 90,
And then went into a skid,
Then was hit by the policeman
(Whose name, I think, was Sid).

And there was a massive pile-up
Of a hundred cars or more,
Who all crashed into each other,
And lay there, door to door.
While further down the motorway
The Meredith family
Carried on quite blithely
To their day out by the sea.

And when they read the paper
The next day, back at base,
Father's mouth dropped open
And a happy smile came to his face.

'We were lucky yesterday, Mother,
When we went down the M.
There were masses of cars in a pile-up –
See this picture of them!'

'What was the cause?' asked Mother.
'Police chase, apparently.
Going too fast in the fast lane
And then – well, you can see.'
'Well, we were lucky,' said Mother
Looking for wood to touch,
And when she said she was lucky,
She didn't know how much.

Now listen, all you drivers,
And harken well to me,
Next time you go to London
Or down the M3 to the sea,
When the police sirens are sounding
And the lights behind are blue,
Ask not whom they are chasing –
The siren blares for you!

10 GREAT MOTORWAY FILMS

No 9.

The Tiny Shop of Horrors

Once there was a motorway service area. And in this service area there was a shop. And in this shop there were things for sale. And these things for sale were the most horrible and useless you could ever imagine. Jane Austen table lamps. Charlotte Brontë fudge. Dogs with illuminated eyes. Soft cuddly snakes. Empty photograph stands which fell over when you touched them. Furry Yeomen of the Guard…

What made it worse was that every other service area had a shop like this as well.

The horrors are everywhere.

BASIC TYPES
of
Motorway Coach

• *Express Coaches*

You know they are Express coaches because they are marked Express, despite the fact that they travel at exactly the same speed as every other non-express coach. They have a notice on the back saying: 'London – Exeter – Now Only £8 Return!' It may not be Exeter. It may be Blackburn or Lincoln. But it is always some place where you do not live and cannot take advantage of travelling to cheaply.

• *Non-Express Coaches*

These are usually marked something like 'W. P. Williams & Son, Penbwlchgwyn, Dyfed, Luxury Coaches', with a telephone and fax number which you never quite catch, because it's actually quite difficult to write down a fax number while driving on the motorway. These coaches always look slightly embarrassed, as if they have strayed on to the motorway by accident and should really be on a day trip to Aberystwyth, or at home knitting.

• *VIP Coaches*

Nobody know who travels in these because they are smooth-sided
monsters with black windows so that nobody can look in and see
the famous people inside. But who *are* these people so famous that
they don't want to be recognised even on the motorway? Are they
Blind Date contestants being shipped up to London? Are they the
remnants of the Parliamentary Tory Party out for a picnic? The
defeated side in the Cup Final slinking back home? The Spice Girls
on tour?

• *Holiday Coaches*

You can always tell when people sitting in a coach are on holiday,
from their dazed look of boredom. They have signed up for a Five
Day Cathedral City tour or a West Country Mystery Tour and have
suddenly realised that most of their time will be spent sitting in a

coach getting from one cathedral city (or West Country beauty spot) to another. What they are actually on is a Motorway Tour. Unfortunately, we have not yet taught ourselves to see motorways as beautiful. (See p. 187 – 'How To Teach Yourself To See Motorways as Beautiful'.)

• *School Coaches*

A school trip is exactly the same as a Saga Holiday outing, except that it is young people instead of old people, and old people are not in the habit of gathering in the back window of their coach and waving at the people behind, let alone making rude gestures, shrieking with laughter and pulling funny faces. All kinds of coaches crash now and then, but it is only when a school coach crashes that it makes news. Is it possible that the school coach you were caught behind for five minutes *was actually the ghost of a coach that crashed here five years ago without any survivors*?

• *Casino Coaches*

Is that what they are? Those coaches with little curtains in each window and little tables in each window and little chintzy table lamps on each table, looking like an old-fashioned bordello, what else could they be but travelling casinos? Yes, someone has surely discovered that by gambling at over 60 mph and moving swiftly from county to county you can evade all the regulations on betting and gaming which apply only to stationary casinos with fixed addresses! That must be it! They're travelling casinos! Unless, of course, they really are old-fashioned bordellos.

• *Period Costume Coaches*

From time to time you may catch sight of a coach on the motorway full of people wearing Jane Austen period costume. It may possibly be some ghastly apparition, but is more likely to be the cast en route to yet another TV Austen adaptation location. But this too is unlikely, as most actors and actresses do not travel in costume. Almost certainly it is a Jane Austen Fan Club ('The Sealed Bodice', perhaps) on an outing to some place where *Pride and Prejudice* has been filmed.

• *Foreign Coaches*

Perhaps 'hotels on wheels' would be a better description, especially of German coaches – if you drive up close behind a German coach, you will see from the specifications on the back that it has on board a minimum of the following facilities: Video, Shower, Toilets, Kitchenette, Washing Machine, Cocktail Bar, Swimming Pool, All-Night Disco. Leaving a four-star coach like this and checking into a mere hotel every night must be a comedown for many Germans. Spanish tour coaches tend to be more like b&bs. Irish coaches are pubs on wheels.

Motorway Nursery Rhymes

THERE WAS A LITTLE CHEF

There was a Little Chef
　　And he had a little wife
And when she was hungry
　　He took his little knife
And he cut a bit of pizza
　　And he put it in the heater
And that's how a Little Chef
　　Makes a Happy Eater

OLD MOTORWAY SAYINGS

When the mist hangs low on Leigh Delamere
Potato fryer is probably on fire

Sorry For Any Delay

A New Motorway Thriller

PART I

Today we start a brand new adventure featuring Hank Mogul, the ever-popular motorway detective. Hank is the only motorway detective there is. That means, he only takes on motorway cases. When a case leaves the motorway, he loses interest. The motorway is the only world that Mogul knows. But in 'Sorry For Any Delay', Hank Mogul reaches parts of the motorway even he didn't know existed…

Hank Mogul drove into the section marked 'Fuel' at the last motorway service area before Scotland that he actually liked, and put the nozzle in his car's inlet pipe. Then he stared around.

Normally, the time when we're filling our car with petrol is the only time we can relax for a moment in our stress-torn lives. We are actually forced to do nothing for once. Hank was surprised that someone like Jane Fonda hadn't put out a book called *Wanna Lose Weight and Gain Inner Peace While You're Filling The Car With Gas? Here's How!* Usually Hank spent the time staring at the petrol pump, thinking how expensive petrol was these days. But this time he had something to do. Specifically, look around for the bloke he was meant to be meeting. He'd had a mystery call saying, 'Meet me at the fuel pumps. I'll be by the car wash. Very important'. Then the phone had slammed down. He'd had no idea who it was, but business was slack. He'd cleared up the case of the disappearing orange cones and wasn't too keen to tackle the threat of the Free Welsh Motorway Army to set fire to the M50. So he thought he might as well…

Then he spotted him. Near where it said: Free Air Pump – Help Yourself. (About once every six months some joker thought it would be a laugh to take a free air pump, and helped himself to it.) There he stood, solidly and stiffly. A plainclothes policeman. Hank Mogul reckoned he could always spot a plainclothes policeman. Villains were difficult – they usually just tried to look like punters, and usually they succeeded. Coppers, on the other hand, made a huge effort above everything else not to look like coppers. So they ended up looking like villains…

'You…?' said Mogul.

The man nodded.

'You're a policeman,' said Hank.

The man sighed.

'I wasn't going to tell you that,' he said. 'Word has got around that you don't like policemen.'

'No, I don't,' said Hank.

'Care to tell me why?'

'Very simple. Three years ago I was in a hurry to get somewhere and there was a policeman driving at a steady 70 mph in front of me. Everyone slowed down to suit him. It caused a huge jam. I didn't get my man.'

'It doesn't seem much to base a life-long dislike of the police on.'

'Not by itself. But it's happened every other day of my life as well.'

But that was not the only reason. There was also the fact that Hank's wife had run off with a policeman. It was the only time in history that someone had run off with a policeman to get someone

121

with more regular working hours. She hadn't come back yet.

'Well, even so, maybe you're the only man who can help us,' said the policeman. 'We've got a problem. We're stumped.'

'Glad to hear it,' said Hank.

'There's a drugs trail that leads to this area. We've trailed a car in several times that contains enough cocaine to fill a nose on Mount Rushmore. We've waited for it to come out again. It's never reappeared. We've searched the car park. It's always gone.'

'There's no way a car could get out without being seen,' said Hank. 'Unless of course it was through the secret access road? The one they bring the sachets of tomato sauce down?'

'Baked Bean Alley? No, we had that covered.'

Baked Bean Alley was the name they gave to the access road used only by lorries bringing in motorway food and taking away motorway litter. To Hank's eye, the volume of each seemed about equal, which didn't say much for the food.

'Well,' said Hank, 'maybe the car drove into the lorry park and was secreted on to a car transporter.'

The policeman stared at him.

'We thought of that. We thought of everything. But still the car vanishes.'

'Why don't you boneheads arrest him as he drives in?'

'Because he's taking us to the bigger fish. We don't want him – we want them.'

Hank laughed. 'It intrigues me. The police have a car surrounded in a car park and it vanishes. The car that could out-think a copper. Yeah, I'll take a look around. I'd like to meet a car that was smarter than a copper.'

'Thanks, Mogul,' said the policeman. 'Here are the details. Now, I think you'd better pay for your petrol and move your car.'

Hank turned round. There were half a dozen cars queueing behind him, most of them hooting. 'They should be relaxing,' said Hank. 'Haven't they read that book by Jane Fonda?'

'Which book?'

'*How To Lose Your Double Chin and Increase Your Hands-on Management Skills While Waiting In Line For Gas…*'

'My boss said you were a crazy fellow,' said the policeman.

'He was right.'

'He also said you got results.'

'Let's wait and see, shall we?' said Hank.

Don't miss the next thrilling episode!

Sorry For Any Delay

PART II

Hank walked round the car park, looking into every corner, knowing that he was unlikely to find anything. It wasn't as if he was going to come across a hitherto unnoticed trap door in the middle of the car park. Cars don't vanish just like that.

Except that this one had.

Strange…

'Care to join the RAC, sir?' asked the RAC man. There were so many of them stationed at motorway service areas that Hank sometimes wondered if anyone was left actually to go out and deal with the breakdowns.

'No, thanks,' said Hank. 'I don't actually drive a car. I'm on a walking tour of the M1.'

'Lord bless you, sir,' said the RAC man, 'you don't actually have to have a car to join the RAC. Everyone is welcome. Lots of social gatherings, Christmas gift ideas, holiday safaris…'

'No, thanks.'

'Or you could join our Hitch-Hiker Get-You-Home service which covers people who have failed to get a hitch after four hours…'

'Get stuffed,' said Hank shortly.

Could you repaint or respray a car in a public car park? Didn't seem likely. Leave paint marks all over the place. Well, could you put a car in a van and drive it off? Not very likely either…

Hank's mind went dizzily round some rather unlikely scenarios (being airlifted out by helicopter was the one he liked best) as he wandered round the car park…

'Ever thought of joining the RAC, sir?'

Blimey, he'd come all the way round again.

'I resigned last week,' said Hank. 'The food was dreadful and the wine list desperately over-priced.'

'Would anything persuade you to rejoin, sir?' said the RAC man, never losing his smile.

'Yes. If you could tell me how someone could spirit a car out of this car park without taking it through the exit, I'd seriously consider joining the RAC.'

'Get a car out of the car park without driving it out?' said the RAC man. 'Well, I should think the best way would be to take it to bits and carry it across the bridge, portion by portion, to the other side. There you could reassemble it and drive away.'

'It's so stupid it could be right,' said Hank. 'I'll be back soon. If you're right, I'll take out a life membership.'

He spent the rest of the day driving to London to go and see a man called Dacre Balsdon, who was a top motorway designer. He had once done a small favour for Balsdon involving a runaway engineer's wife (she had run away to a rival firm, taking some bridge designs with her) and Balsdon had said that Hank could call in any time. Now he was going to call in, even if Dacre Baldson couldn't remember who the hell he was.

But Balsdon could remember who the hell he was. 'Mogul, my dear fellow, how good to see you! How may I help you?'

'Balsdon, if you had to get a car from one side of a motorway service to the other without anyone noticing, how would you do it? Someone's doing it and we don't know how.'

'Which service area is it?'

'Tatternall Bagley.'

'That's interesting.'

'What's interesting about it?'

'Tatternall Bagley is one of the ones with a tunnel.'

'With a *what*?'

'Didn't you know? Oh, there's more than one way to join the two sides of a motorway service area. It's always been galling to us motorway designers that the public can just cross a footbridge to the other side but that there's no link for the people who actually run the place. So we thought of putting in a secret tunnel… You can't do it with new motorway service areas. You can't, in other words, tunnel under a pre-existing motorway. But if the area is built at the same time as the roadway, Bob's your uncle. Tatternall Bagley was one of the early original ones. Purely for service reasons, it has actually got a large underground tunnel.'

'I'm amazed I never knew that,' said Hank.

'After we had it built,' said Balsdon, 'we had all the people who worked on it taken out and shot. Basic security measure, Mogul.'

'Very funny, Balsdon,' said Hank. He said goodbye, and didn't stop driving untl he was back at Tatternall Bagley. There he nosed around the back of the service area buildings and came across a large grating he had never noticed before, but which was on the plans Balsdon had lent him. He pulled at it slightly. It came away slightly. He pulled at it a lot. It came away a lot. Then it came away in his hands.

There was a staircase in there, and a lift shaft. He went silently down the staircase and came to a large space in which an extraordinary sight met his eyes. Four RAC men were pushing a small car into a tunnel. He could tell at once that they were not real RAC men. Real RAC men don't wear guns, for a start.

'What the bloody hell…!' said one, seeing Hank.

'I just popped in to ask about becoming an RAC member,' said Hank, 'but I feel I may have come at an inopportune moment…'

He made as if to leave. He stopped when he felt a hard object in his back. It was a gun held by the RAC man from upstairs, no longer smiling.

'I might have known it. You're the nosey parker who wanted to know how to get a car from one side of the motorway to the other without being spotted, ain't you? Well, now you know. And I'm afraid you won't be telling anyone else…'

There was a sort of explosion inside Hank's head as the gun butt descended. His last thought was: When they search me, I hope they won't be too cross when they find my AA membership card…

Want to know what happens next? Then rush out and get the new Hank Mogul thriller, 'Sorry For Any Delay'.

10 GREAT MOTORWAY FILMS

No 10.
The Big Bus

Jim didn't pay attention much when the big bus cut in in front of him. He had been overtaken by many big coaches before. He didn't pay much heed when the teenage girls waved at him from the back of the bus. Almost every coach on the motorway seemed to contain bored teenagers in the back window. But when the girl on the left fixed him with her glinting stare and seemed to be looking straight into him, and when he felt his fingers respond to some unspoken command, he started to pay heed.

Unfortunately, it was too late…

'That's the fifth unexplained fatal crash on the M this week,' said Inspector Wildmsith. 'And that big bus has been there every time. There can't be any connection. And yet I wonder…'

The
Brief Ballad
of
Alan Clark

Alan Clark drove in the dark
Scattering slower souls.
He drove so fast
He went right past
Two lurking police patrols.

'OK,' said The Bill, 'with luck we will
Arrest that joker there.'
'Don't you know who I am?'
Said Clark, in a jam,
'No, we don't, and we sodding don't care.'

Alan Clark was forced to park
His Porsche for a very long time.
And if he was caught,
What chance have *you* got?
So, remember, speeding's a crime.

PETROL PUMP GIRL

I've fallen in love with a girl who sells petrol,
She sits at the till which says 'Pumps 1–9',
And if I can possibly buy enough fuel,
That motorway salesgirl will one day be mine!

Whenever I give her my Access so shyly
And she smiles back at me and says, 'Anything else?',
I want to shout, 'Yes! I would like to go dancing
And swirl you around till we hear wedding bells!'

But all I can say is, 'A packet of wine gums
And receipt for VAT purposes, please.'
She holds up the company's petrol gift vouchers
And says, like an angel, 'Do you take these?'

Oh, why can I not throw all caution aside?
Why must I always sit on the fence?
Why do I never just tell her I love her?
Why do I always say, 'Please, where is the gents?'

I've fallen in love with the girl who takes plastic
The loveliest girl that I've ever seen,
Whom I first met when serving pumps 1–9,
But has now been promoted to 10–18.

I buy so much petrol and fags and sweeties
That I fear by the time I've captured her heart
I'll be fat and skint and reek of tobacco,
And be selling my car through *Exchange and Mart*.

Oh, I've fallen in love with the girl who sells petrol
But I fear that to her I'm a face in the queue,
Just another man smiling, and jingling his car keys
And asking directions to go to the loo…

MOTORWAY'S RUTHLESS RHYMES

PETER THE MAP READER

Peter tried to read the map,
On his knees, at 95.
He was a decent sort of a chap.
I'm sorry he's no longer alive.

CRASH

The film 'Crash' elicited an excited response from the public's spokespersons when awarded a general release and is still out there somewhere, going along at 90mph with no signals.

Is it controversial to link cars with sex? Yet there is nothing new about the whole field of motoring psychosexual behaviour, or limopsychology. As early as the 1920s, the novelist William Faulkner observed that many men lavished on their cars the sort of affectionate grooming that used to go on their wives, and was it not Scott Fitzgerald who observed that the two great innovators of the twentieth century had almost the same name, Freud and Ford?

Yes, human behaviour *is* altered by the presence of cars, and a whole new branch of psychology has grown up to explore this phenomenon. Foremost among the experts in the field is Dr Dion-Bouton, who joins us today to deal with some of the emotional inquiries which have flooded into my office over the weekend, causing tailbacks and delays which have taken days to clear up. All yours, Doc!

I gather that this film 'Crash' is about people who get some sort of sexual turn-on from watching car crashes. Well, this may well happen, I don't know. What I do know is that I have the opposite condition. By which I mean that whenever I am engaged in sexual activity, which I have to say I

*do not find very exciting per se, I find myself thinking of the far more
arousing subject of cars and driving.*

*Typically, when I am in bed with my girl-friend, I suddenly find myself
in my imagination driving a Bentley or a Jaguar at terrific speeds through
rush hour traffic, scattering everything in my passage, and I find this
wonderfully voluptuous. Then, so my girl-friend tells me, I cry out
something like 'Get out of the way! I'm coming through on the inside!', or
'Mind your backsides on the hard shoulder!' and of course she gets alarmed
and shakes me, and I come back to my senses and I find I am not driving a
car at all but just in bed with a girl. Then I get up and make a cup of tea. Is
there something wrong with me?*

Dr Dion-Bouton writes: No. You have your head well screwed
on. Sex is a shoddy, risky business, but you know where you are
with a good car.

*I find I also have the opposite reaction to the people in the film called
'Crash' but in a different way. They may be sexually aroused by crashes,
but I am sexually aroused by traffic jams. Whenever I am in a long tailback
I get these very lascivious thoughts and I want to stretch out in the back of
the car with my partner and do naughty things, but as soon as the traffic
picks up again I lose all desire for hanky panky and become calm and
focused on driving again. My ultimate dream would be to see a
controversial sex film called 'Gridblock!' in which no cars moved at all. Is
there anything wrong with this?*

Dr Dion-Bouton writes: Yes, you are a very sick woman. You
seem to have some sort of control fixation whereby you wish your
car to give you a completely subservient attitude, and to dominate
it. But a relationship with a car is based on equality, observing each
other's needs. This talk of 'hanky panky' and 'naughty things'
betrays your infantile regression. Grow up and love your car
properly!

I am very interested in what Steve Norris has been saying about his change of mind on the Newbury By-Pass. If you remember, he was a transport minister who was famous for two things: for having lots of mistresses and for liking cars a lot. Nowadays we don't hear about his mistresses any more – he has suddenly become famous for his recantation on roads, for saying that more roads only produces more traffic. Are you impressed by his turn against cars?

Dr Dion-Bouton writes: No. I am only impressed by your failure to put two and two together Here is a man who seems to lose interest in sex *and* in cars at the same time, and you are surprised? But if you take the basic premise of limopsychology – namely that sex and cars are intimately bound together -then there can be no surprise at all.

If what you say about sex and cars were true, there would be some tell-tale phallic element in driving. If you can name just one, I will be convinced.

Dr Dion-Bouton writes: Phallic symbol in driving? Have you ever seen the winner of a Grand Prix take a bottle of champagne and shake it till it emits froth?

I am convinced.

Dr Dion-Bouton will be back again soon, if he drives carefully.

134

Oh, She's the Queen of Taunton Deane...

Oh, she's the Queen
Of Taunton Deane,
Prettiest girl I've ever seen!
My heart's ablaze
When she wipes the trays
And clears away the last baked bean.

I've been to Newport Pagnell
And visited Michael Wood,
South Mimms, Aust and Gordano,
And all of them were good,

But there's no one there
Who can compare
With my angel in blue jean –
That bit of heaven
En route to Devon
Who works at Taunton Deane!

Membury and Chievely
Leigh Delamere and Fleet –
All of them are lovely,
But there's one that's got them beat!

'Cos if you've never been
To Taunton Deane
Then you've never seen my motorway queen!
She's taken my tray
And my heart away
And wiped them both so shiny clean!

135

Ballad of the Lost Motorway

Oh, listen, you maidens,
   And hearken to me
And don't you drive down
   The M33!

For many young policemen
   And RAC men
Who went down that road
   Were not seen again !

The signs are so tempting
   Saying: 'Turn off ahead',
But don't you obey them
   Or you might end up dead.

One night as I motored
   Along the M6
I saw a big signpost:
   'Exit Here For The Styx'

On The M33,
   One mile ahead',
And I wish now I'd driven
   Straight home instead.

But inquisitive, I turned off,
   Although it was dark,
And found a great river
   Running through a great park.

And the boatman said, 'Hi there!
   You coming with me?'
And I said I was looking
   For the M33.

'I'll take you,' he said,
   With a skull-like grin
But I ran to my car
   And jumped right in,

And drove back again
   The way I had come
To the distant sound
   Of a funeral drum...

Behind me the terror,
   Ahead the light –
I drove quite reckless
   Through the night!

Till I came back down
    The same exit road
And only then
    Relaxed and slowed,

When suddenly out
    Of the dark, dark night
There came a familiar
    Flashing blue light.

'Hello,' said the policeman,
    'And what have we here?
Parked on the shoulder?
    Oh dear, oh dear...

'A little bit drunk, sir?
    Or having a snooze?
It's not what I'd call
    A good place to choose...'

So I told him the truth
    Of where I'd just been,
And he said, 'I know no one
    Who's seen what you've seen,

'For the road that you speak of
    Does not exist!
It's all been a dream, sir.
    Are you sure you're not pissed?'

Not a drink had I taken,
    Not a wink had I slept,
And I showed him the mileage
    I'd carefully kept.

It proved that I'd driven
    Twenty miles more
Than my scheduled journey
    Door to door!

'I believe what you say,'
    Said the man in blue,
'But you must tell no one
    What I now tell you,

'For the M33
    Is a ghost motorway.
Here tomorrow,
    And gone today!

'No atlas shows it,
    No gazetteer,
It comes and it goes –
    It's usually not there...'

And I must have dozed off
    As he wandered on,
For when I awoke
    That policeman had gone!

And I started in horror,
    Then turned on the car,
And didn't look back
    Till I'd gone very far,

And that's why I say,
    Oh, Listen to me,
And ignore all those signposts
    Saying, 'M33'!

THINKING
and
DRIVING

Oscar Tankard has been called the Philosopher of the Motorway. He has always tried to get behind the simple façade of motorway life and tease out the secrets hidden behind what seems to be the mere act of piling up and down a long road at 70 mph.

His thoughts on motorway driving, published in the best-selling book, *I Think Therefore I Drive*, have been published in seventeen languages. Here is a selection of just a few.

Most motorways go through countryside most of the time. This is because motorways are built to join towns together and have to go through countryside to get from one town to another. *No motorway was ever built to join one bit of countryside to another.*

Not only do motorways go through countryside most of the time, they go through *boring* countryside most of the time. This is because it is cheaper to build motorways in boring countryside (such as rolling farmland) than in interesting countryside (rocky glens, high mountains, cliff tops with great views over the Channel, etc.).

The reason people fall asleep on the motorway is because of the boring scenery. People never go to sleep on highways in Switzerland. Anyone who falls asleep on a motorway should sue the makers.

We all know what the central reservation is, but no one knows what it is reserved for.

The most interesting thing about the motorway link between North and South Wales is that there isn't one. This is not because it would be difficult to build. It is because North and South Wales have absolutely no desire to be linked.

Why do motorways have no names? Numbers, yes, but never names. In the old days we had the Great North Road and the Bath Road, and even in America they had the Pompton Turnpike. But what do we have now? The A1(M)? Where is the poetry in a couple of brackets?

The only numbered road that ever sounded remotely romantic was Route 66.

The most ridiculous thing in the world – a line of concrete lamp stands stretching along a motorway far out into the countryside, *and one of them still on*, even though it is midday.

What if you broke down on the motorway, walked for a mile looking for help, saw an emergency phone at last, approached it – and it started ringing as you got to it!

A motorway is the only place in the world where, as you are driving along, there is always this dark thought lurking in the recesses of your mind: 'What would I do if an aeroplane made an emergency landing on my side of the motorway? *Behind me?*'

There are never any climbing plants on motorway bridges. Is this because plants do not like concrete, or because all creepers are removed at night?

After a big motorway pile-up, especially in rain or fog. the police always say: 'They were driving like maniacs.' Nobody ever objects to this. In other words, motorways are the last refuge of political incorrectness. No one is allowed to call people maniacs or lunatics any more. You would have to say: 'They were driving like people with a temporarily altered view of the world', or 'like people with a sad history of mental instability in the family'.

Nor is anybody ever said to be driving like a 'serial killer'. A serial killer would, presumably, drive very carefully. The last thing he wants on his hands is an unplanned death.

You cannot see any butterflies when you are driving on a motorway. They are there all right, but when you are going at 70 mph and they are going at one mph, you are going too fast to see them. All neighbouring animals become invisible at a certain speed of travel: fleas at two mph, cows at 1,000 mph…

In fact, there are some things that are visible only when you are stationary. The motion of clouds, for instance. When you are standing still you can easily see the clouds moving, but as soon as you start moving, you cannot tell what direction they are going in. A driver on the motorway always gets the impression that clouds are moving at about 70 mph, but he knows this is an illusion so

he corrects for it – and imagines they are not moving at all, which is also wrong.

The ministry often puts up notices saying, 'Sorry For Any Delay', but no motorist ever puts one up saying, 'That's All Right – Don't Mention It.'

A clergyman once told me about his problem.

'I believe in the Trinity,' he said, 'but I find it very hard to convince other people that God can really be Three in One and One in Three.'

'Try using imagery,' I said.

'Yes, but what image can I use for the Trinity?' he asked.

'Try the image of a three-lane motorway,' I suggested. 'There you have it! Three lanes, all separate, but all united to make one roadway on which everyone can go forward to their own destiny!'

'Very good,' said the cleric. 'I'll try that!'

Later I met him again.

'Did you try it?' I asked.

'Yes,' he said glumly. 'But everyone wanted to know why a three-lane Trinity was coming back on the other side as well.'

Motorway Nursery Rhymes

THERE WAS A LITTLE MAN

There was a little man
　And he had a little van
With the back door tied
　Together with rope,
And when the rope broke
　It wasn't a joke
Because he shed a load
　Of Colombian dope…

OLD MOTORWAY SAYINGS

Breakfast time at Watford Gap
Lucky to get your tea on Shap

Prayers for Use on the Motorway

A Prayer for Children

O Lord, look down I pray upon little children everywhere, and especially in our own vehicle, and give them the gift of silence, also the gifts of patience, and of abstinence, and of good cheer, and of obedience, but of these the greatest is obedience, or maybe silence, yes, definitely silence, road without end, Amen.

A Prayer for Farmers

O Lord, we beseech thee at this time to look down upon farmers everywhere and keep them off the motorway, so that they will not shed their load of straw bales, or drive very slowly right in front of me or pull out without signalling.

A Prayer for Rain

O Lord, forasmuch as I am listening to the Test Match on the radio while travelling on the A1(M) and it is pouring down cats and dogs here, but over in Edgbaston it is bright and sunny, and forasmuch as the Australians are beating the English hollow, therefore at this time feel free to take this rain from here and pour it all on Birmingham.

A Pray to be Used in a Time of Motorway Tailback

O Lord, whereas at this time we can see only the brightness of stationary traffic ahead of us and no end to the jam in sight, and although we have tuned in to the local radio station as urged to do on the placards lining the motorway in an effort to search out a

cause for this obstruction, and have yet been unable to discover anything except that country 'n' western music is very popular in these parts, and that there is a fantastic sale on at a nearby DIY store whose name I failed to catch, look down now upon us and melt this traffic jam, so that we can sail through and reach our destination not later than nightfall, and as we sail through let us see some good reason for this almighty hold-up such as a car joyously ablaze or a lorry which has shed its load of frilly pink nighties, instead of the usual absence of any clue for this snarl-up, for thine is the carriageway, the slip road and hard shoulder…

A Prayer to Avert Arson

O Lord, whereas it has pleased thee to let me just now drop a lighted cigarette through the steering wheel, grant me at this time the power to locate and retrieve it without crashing, or, failing that, to let the cigarette be extinguished without setting fire to the car, and in return we do solemnly swear that this will be our last cigarette ever, we know we have solemnly sworn this before, but this time we really mean it, please hurry because we swear we can smell burning, world without end, Amen.

A Prayer for Better Understanding Between Motorists

O Lord, forasmuch as you can see into all people's hearts, please see into the heart of the man in front of me who has been in the middle lane from the time we joined the motorway, and ascertain whether there is any good reason why he should be driving in the middle lane, and if there be not, I pray you to drop a thunder bolt on him, and a second one if the first one work not.

A Prayer for Peace

O Lord, whereas the generations do battle, and male sets his hand against female, and those of little faith shout out that we have passed our exit, and children cry that they are hungry and grandparents that they desire a rest, and I say nothing but all are set against me, make there to be a SUDDEN SILENCE in this car for the space of upward of an hour so that I can hear myself speak before I am driven to thoughts of violence.

OLD MOTORWAY SAYINGS

Gridlock at Scotch Corner
Car like a sauna
Gridlock at Aust
Beware your exhaust
But if you're stuck at Michaelwood
You're probably gone for good

Ballad of the Cardboard Policeman

I've fallen in love with a cardboard policeman,
Who sits in state up on bridge 28,
I love his cut-out panda squad car
And his cardboard profile is simply great!
He sits all day in isolation
And the motorists down below go slow
Whenever they see his warning profile
But he always sets my heart aglow.

Oh , Mr Policeman, come down to me,
Near exit Number 23,
And tell me to pull into the side
And get my licence ratified!

I've fallen in love with a cardboard policeman
But it's not an artificial love.
It's the real, true thing from me down here
To my cardboard lover up above.
To you he may be synthetic stuff,
But to me he's plenty real enough.
And in my dreams he comes to life,
And asks me to be his cardboard wife!

Pride and Prudence

(With apologies to Jane Austen)

*I*t is a truth universally acknowledged that when a single woman is stranded on the side of a motorway with a stricken car, and a young man with no marital ties stops to offer her help, she would be well advised at the very least to ask to see his credentials.

So it was that when Catherine Dodson had been standing by her Montego for twenty-five minutes, watching the plumes of steam arise from the radiator and noticing with horror a trickle of what she took to be oil coming from under the body of the car, she was not best pleased to spy a small blue van marked RAC pull up and come to a halt very near to her. She was even less pleased when a young man in uniform emerged from the driving seat wiping his hands and smiling.

'Having a bit of trouble, miss?' he called.

Miss Dodson stiffened slightly. She was not in the habit of being addressed so familiarly by bachelors to whom she had not been formally introduced. 'I don't believe I have had the pleasure,' she said.

'Nor have I recently,' he said, guffawing somewhat roughly, but growing quiet when he saw she did not laugh. 'Sorry if that was a bit out of order, miss,' he continued. 'Name's Ramsay, if you want to know, Harry Ramsay, I was just passing with no particular job to go to and saw you were in a bit of trouble, so I stopped.'

Miss Catherine Dodson took in this flood of information and decided that, although he was rough of speech and dress, he seemed to be kindly inclined and, beside, one never knew what large private income might be possessed by the most unlikely people. So she ventured a cautious reply. 'Have you resided in this area long?'

Mr Ramsay looked round the area and back at her. 'No, miss. Just passing through. On my way to London.'

'London!' said Miss Dodson. 'It is not everyone who can afford to reside in London. I have an aunt who has a small house in Lowndes Square and she complains unceasingly that she does not know how much longer she can go on living there.'

'Not surprised,' said Mr Ramsay. 'Posh bit of town that is. Costs more to park there than it does to live in Barking.'

'Barking?' said Miss Dodson faintly. 'Where is Barking?'

'On the way out to Essex.'

'Essex? I don't think I know…'

'Look, perhaps I should just have a shufti at your engine,' said Harry Ramsay.

'I am not so very sure I should let a total stranger have a look at my engine,' said Catherine Dodson, mindful of her parents' constant admonition never to embark on any social entanglement which might lead to a proposal of marriage from a gentleman with an annual income of less than £20,000 a year, 'though we might reduce that to a sum nearer £15,000 as you advance into your thirties, Catherine,' her father had once joked, not unmaliciously.

'Suit yourself,' said the RAC man. 'But I would have thought that the chances of someone well-known to you coming along and helping you out were on the low side.'

'There is a certain truth in what you say,' admitted Catherine.

'And I am not so sure I would like to be a young lady standing all alone with a car that doesn't work on the side of a motorway these days, not after all the stories you hear.'

Catherine was about to inquire what all these stories were that you heard these days, but some sixth ladylike sense warned her that they might not be fit for her ears.

'So when someone from our organisation stops, you'd be sensible to take advantage of it, I'd have thought.'

'What organisation is that, pray?'

Harry Ramsay nodded at his van. 'RAC. Royal Automobile Club.'

'Royal Automobile Club,' echoed Catherine. 'You are under the patronage of the Royal Family?'

'Very much so,' said Harry Ramsay. 'I should say so.'

'You move in very high circles indeed,' said Catherine. 'I have never so much as met a duke, and here you are, hobnobbing with royalty.'

'I mended a fuse for a Right Hon, once,' said Harry trying to sound modest, 'and I was once called to the scene of a non-functioning car belonging to a titled lady, only it turned out she was just out of petrol, that's all.'

Catherine Dodson was very rapidly revising her opinion of this young man. He was remarkably well connected, considering his dirty uniform, and yet even his uniform was not unmanly, she considered. Were he also to turn out to be in possession of an adequate income, this knight of the road, there might be every conceivable advantage in pursuing his acquaintance. 'It is a long way to go to London,' she said. 'Perhaps you should consider the merits of pausing here for refreshment at my parents' house which is not far from here…'

How Mr Ramsay mended Miss Dodson's fan belt, how he was entertained to tea by the Dodsons, how Mr Ramsay imagined that he was falling in love with Catherine's sister Harriet and how Mr and Mrs Dodson viewed the prospect of a son-in-law who actually seemed to work for a living, shall all be related in due course.

MOTORWAY'S RUTHLESS RHYMES

HENRY AND HIS AUNT

Henry said to his aunt, 'I'm blowed!
We've just missed our exit road!
I'll back up the entrance, see if I can't!'
Goodbye, Henry. Goodbye, aunt.

Motorway Nursery Rhymes

LITTLE JOHNNY

Little Johnny had a lorry
To which he was so unkind
Wherever little Johnny went
It shed its load behind.

OLD MOTORWAY SAYINGS

If you come to Potter's Bar,
Chances are you've gone too far.
If you see a sign to Aust,
It's a sign you're totally lost.
And if you come to Clacket Lane,
You would best turn back again.
But if you come upon South Mimms
The time has come to sing your hymns.

The Song of the Mystified Motorist

Oh, I've been going up the
    motorway
For nigh on thirty year,
I've listened to the radio
Till it's coming out my ear.
I've been up every exit
And gone down every lane,
I've been around the M25
(I'm not doing that again).

I've talked to many a driver
And listened to many a tale
Of what happens on the motorway
When the warning beacons fail.
And many a ghost yarn have I
    heard
And many a mystery,
But there's one thing on the
    motorway
Which remains a puzzle to me:

Why on earth do lorries
Always flash their lights?
What does it mean
When they turn on their beam
As they get you in their sights?

Do they have a secret language
Which we can never share?
One flash for 'Hi!'
Two for 'Goodbye'
And three for 'Your tyres need
    air'?

Are they saying 'Hello stranger',
Or 'Blimey, your car needs a
    wash',
Or have they just said:
'Don't turn off ahead –
They serve really terrible
    nosh'?

I wish I knew why lorries
Flash us from behind.
Why, when we pass,
Do they dazzle our glass
And nearly turn us blind?

What are they trying to tell us?
Are they trying to remonstrate
For some awful mistake?
Or keep us awake?
Or is it a message of hate?

Is *that* what they're trying to tell
    us?
A message of hate to all cars?
Is it something I said?
Should I give way instead?
Is it something to do with class?

Should I *smile* when I pass a lorry
And wave, and shout 'All right!'?
If I act like a friend
Will he let me wend
My way with no blast of light?

Do lorries really hate us
Because we're not all slow?
Would they really prefer us
To drive like a hearse?
I hope the answer's no...

Maybe lorries are lonely
And trying to communicate.
Maybe they're flashing
To get some compassion
Or asking us for a date!

Oh, tell me, why do lorries
Turn on and off their light.
Evening and morning,
When day is dawning,
Or odd times through the night?

And why do I feel guilty
When they flash at me?
What have I gone
And been and done?
Is there something I can't see?

Oh, I've been on all the
    motorways
In every sort of car
In Saabs and Fiats
From Stoke to St Neots
And even, once, to Armagh.

I've talked to old folk in cafés
And ancient AA men,
I've consulted the runes
And know all the tunes
And heard the midnight Big Ben

Yes, I have got a clean licence
And I can hold my hooch,
I know this land
Like the back of my hand –
I can spell Ashby-de-la-Zouche.

But one thing's got me worried
One thing's got me perplexed –
Why, oh why,
As you go by,
Does the lorry flash you next?

155

8
Typical Motorway Lorry Drivers

DAVE

Dave is listening to Radio 1. Well, he has got Radio 1 on in his cab. He has always got Radio 1 on in his cab. He doesn't really listen to it. In fact, he doesn't know it is there. He only knows when it is not there. He only really hears Radio 1 when it is off. He once picked up a student hitch-hiker

156

who asked Dave if he might listen to the Test Match for a moment
to get the score and retuned the radio to Radio 3. It was still on
Radio 3 when he let the student go. It took Dave three weeks to get
it back to Radio 1. As soon as he had found Radio 1 again he
heaved a huge sigh of relief and stopped listening to it. He has
never picked up a hitch-hiker since.

ANGUS

His real name is not Angus, it is Phil, but one of the other drivers
once spotted that he somewhat resembled Angus Deayton and
nicknamed him Angus and the name stuck. Actually, he is not as
goodlooking as Angus Deayton, but then, neither is Angus
Deayton. Ever since he was nicknamed Angus he has started
unconsciously dressing more smartly to suit the image of his
nickname and even went to a party last Christmas wearing a bow-
tie. Unfortunately, he is starting to go bald rather faster than Angus
Deayton is, and he is faced with the prospect that in ten years time
he will look nothing like him at all. He dreads acquiring the
nickname Hislop.

EDDIE

Eddie spends most of the lonely hours at the wheel staring into
space and having active sex fantasies. At the moment he is
fantasising that he has stopped to offer help to a young attractive
woman motorist on a lonely B Road who has broken down. He
manages to mend her broken fan belt and she is so grateful that she
starts undressing him, making it clear that her gratitude is going to
take unusual forms. Just when he has lost the last shred of
clothing, three other women, including his wife, appear from
nowhere, call him very rude names, jeer at him, grab his clothing
and drive off with the woman in her car, leaving him naked and

helpless. Yes, Eddie's fantasy life is very guilt-ridden, but some people might say it was at least better than Radio 1.

MARTIN

Martin used to be a tank driver in the Army, and when he came out he looked for a job which would give him the same camaraderie, the same solitude, the same ability to travel and the same loud noises without the same risk of being killed. Compared to his days in tanks, lorry driving seems very fast indeed, but he is irked by having to stick to the road. Whenever he gets caught in a motorway jam, he is fiercely tempted to drive down the verge, crash through the fence and charge across the field, which would be child's play in a tank, but not so easy in a lorry. When cars overtake him, he often presses an imaginary gun button and blows them up in huge balls of fire.

URSULA

Not many long distance lorry drivers are women, and very few are named after a fourth-century Christian saint who was (allegedly) martyred in Cologne along with 11,000 other virgins. Occasionally bones are dug up in Cologne which might well be the remains of St Ursula. There again, they might be one of the 11,000 virgins. None of this concerns Ursula the long-distance lorry driver who is more worried about her martyrdom at the hands of the 11,000 male lorry drivers she seems to encounter every day.

BEN

Ben was once caught in a French seamen's strike outside Dieppe for five days and spent the whole time planning what tattoo he was going to have put on him when he got back. He now spends most of the time on the motorway wondering if it is worth going to all the pain, expense and bother of getting rid of the large dragon on his chest.

JULIAN

Julian is an Arts Graduate from a good university. To put it another way, he did three months work on art history in three years and was lucky to get a degree. He was also lucky to get a job driving a lorry, for which he had to lie about his age, experience, degree and his name, as everyone thinks he is called Junior. He spends his time in the cab doing an Open University course on ecology and is slowly becoming convinced that the damage caused by lorry drivers like himself is ruining the planet. He may not last long in the job.

FRED

In his own small way Fred is an intellectual manqué, being an addict of puzzles and crosswords. At the moment he is obsessed by anagrams. Like most people, he is keenly aware of how many lorries on the motorway chain are owned by Eddie Stobart. Unlike most people, whenever he sees a lorry marked Eddie Stobart he spends the next twenty miles trying to think of an anagram for Eddie Stobart. So far he has not thought of one (though he quite likes 'breddie toast') but he has managed to think of over a hundred words formed by the letters in the name 'Eddie Stobart'.